Songs of PEACE, FREEDOM, and PROTEST

Collected and Edited with Notes by
Tom Glazer

DAVID McKAY COMPANY, INC.
New York

Second Printing, October 1971

SONGS OF PEACE, FREEDOM, AND PROTEST

LIBRARY OF CONGRESS CATALOG CARD NUMBER: 70–114739
MANUFACTURED IN THE UNITED STATES OF AMERICA

Songs of
Peace, Freedom,
and Protest

To the innocent victims of oppression everywhere; to those who rot in jails all over the world because of their love of freedom and democracy; to the sufferers of religious bigotry and to those who lack freedom of worship; to the pawns in war games; to the human victims of unasked-for aggression; to the hungry the starving, and the poor without hope—and to the makers of these songs, this book is dedicated.

Contents

INTRODUCTION

Songs are just as fugitive in our minds as they are insistent. This is true regardless, it seems, of their quality. Good songs can be ignored or forgotten; an ordinary song may creep unbidden into the mind out of unconscious depths at the most random instant.

Before the world sped up to its present dizzying pace (every age says the same thing about its own time), it was rather easy to keep up with the current popular hits, on or off Broadway, or from other countries. But after World War II, with the emergence of the Affluent Society and of the prosperous teenager as consumer and purveyor of popular music, it became more and more difficult even for experts and professionals to keep up with all the fascinating variety of songs and trends in popular music.

Without attempting a historical survey in depth, one might cite the following important highlights of the past forty-odd years:

The United States, a baby country in age, became old enough for an interest in its folksongs to develop. Collectors —Carl Sandburg, the Lomaxes, and others—began to publish the rich store of material. The Archive of American Folksong at the Library of Congress became a stimulus and repository.

Professional folksingers emerged: Carl Sandburg, Burl Ives, Richard Dyer-Bennett, the Almanac Singers, Woody Guthrie, Pete Seeger, and others.

The great Depression of the 1930s and its attendant rise of the labor union produced the first enthusiastic sponsor of folksongs and folksinging and protest songwriting.

The struggles of the Negro after World War II for a better stake and shake in America focussed new and sharper attention on black music, folk and popular. The integration movements were reflected in a new integration of musical styles: Hillbilly or Country and Western (white), Rhythm and Blues (black), jazz (both), Folk (both), Broadway theater music (mostly white), and Tin Pan Alley Pop (both). I recall standing around one afternoon in a popular music publisher's office off Tin Pan Alley, listening to a singer on an obscure record label, Sun Records, Tennessee. Everyone there was wondering —being trend-spotters for business reasons—why the record was selling so well. The singer, who sounded like a Negro to everyone there, was Elvis Presley. And today, a new black Country and Western singer named Charley Pride is beginning to make a big name for himself. He sounds like a younger version of Eddy Arnold, still a big white star.

Those older styles, in varying blendings, became Rock and Roll, Rockabilly, Folk Rock, Hard Rock, Art Rock, and so on. The Beatles, at first nothing more or less than Elvis Presley multiplied by four, but with their own songwriting talent, made something new of a borrowed style. Bob Dylan, sprung from the musical origin of Woody Guthrie, added his songwriting talent to his borrowed playing and singing style, concentrating first on protest songs.

The brand-new, unprecedented Peace, Freedom, and Protest song, as popular as the older hit tunes, is a phenomenon hardly to be believed. Songs like "Blowin' in the Wind," "Where Have All the Flowers Gone," "If I Had a Hammer" appearing on the top ten or twenty list of hits astonished the old-time song publishers and songwriters, who had hitherto been accustomed to love songs.

All these factors, then, plus a Revolution in Realism, if I may call it that, created a situation that was directly reflected in popular song. The Beatniks sang. The Hippies sang. The Freedom Marchers sang in and out of jail. The Protesters sang. The poets sang. The singers wrote poems. Groups formed, broke up, and re-formed. Politicians, to the stupefaction of their constituents, sang. It was really something to see political types, ordinarily accustomed only to oratory, linking arms, swaying, and singing "We Shall Overcome." Even the war in Vietnam, which in its more tolerated days won no popularity contests, produced one hit song, "The Green Berets." The Democrats sang and the Republicans sang. In fact, the Republican National Convention, back in 1948 and 1952, was not too confused to listen to a rendition of "Ballad For Americans," which no doubt did confuse its "progressive" writers.

And the guitar, that innocent and beautiful instrument, which Beethoven had called a symphony orchestra in itself, spread like the locust over the land.

The songs in this book are by no means confined to those of the recent past. They range in time from "Jefferson and Liberty," sung first in 1800, to the hit song of 1968, "Abraham, Martin and John," which tells about the martyrdom of Abraham Lincoln, John and Robert Kennedy, and Martin Luther King, Jr.

Contained within this span, and comprising various types, are familiar older songs, which in my opinion cannot be reprinted too often, for the famous song of yesterday (not unlike any famous personage of yesterday) is the unfamiliar song of today. There are a few songs that I believe have never been printed before, and are very unfamiliar, if not virtually unknown. There are songs from several periods of crisis: the Depression of the 1930s, several wars old and new, the Freedom Movements of the 1960s. There are union songs, mainly, alas, from the lean, hungry, organizing days of yore. There are spirituals both old and modernized. There are anonymous songs and songs by the major protest songwriters of today: Bob Dylan, Woody Guthrie, Pete Seeger, Lee Hays, Phil Ochs, Malvina Reynolds, Tom Paxton, and Tom Lehrer. There are contemporary hit songs and old ragtime tunes. There are parodies and parodies of parodies. And there is a sprinkling of foreign songs.

Due to some insurmountable difficulties of copyright, a few fine songs had to be left out: Woody Guthrie's "This Land Is Your Land," Bob Dylan's "Masters of War," "The Times They Are A-Changin'," "Blowin' in the Wind." All the good songs that were available could not be included, for this collection was meant not so much to be all-inclusive as it was to be a treasury.

There is one type of song that I have not mentioned until now because it requires a paragraph to itself. I have included several examples of songs that are not really protest songs in the political sense, but might be called songs of social protest. These are usually humorous or lugubrious songs, and I hope I don't have to apologize for them by having somewhat stretched the meaning of the word protest. They leaven a little the sadness of the peace songs, the seriousness of the freedom songs, and the sobriety of the political protest songs.

Finally, I have the pleasant duty to thank the following men and women for their invaluable help: Joy Graeme, Harry Fleishman, Al Brackman, Sally Oppenheim, Nancy Klevan, Irwin Silber, Mary Cruddock, Owen Fleishman, Michael Flanders, Alex Comfort, Donna West, Lee Schryver, and others.

Scarborough, N.Y., January 1970

Songs of
Peace, Freedom,
and Protest

ABRAHAM, MARTIN AND JOHN

By DICK HOLLER

A most affecting rock and roll hit in 1968, sung by Dion (Dimucci), formerly Dion and the Belmonts, on Laurie Records. From the look of this song, it seems too simple to be of much interest, but try to listen to Dion sing it on his hit record.

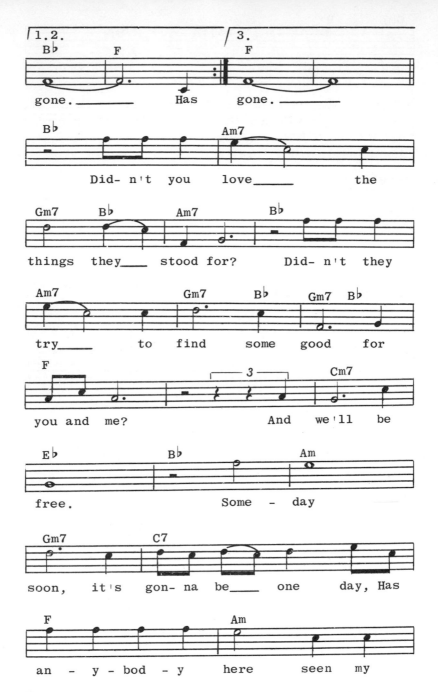

gone. _____ Has gone. _____

Did- n't you love_____ the

things they___ stood for? Did- n't they

try_____ to find some good for

you and me? And we'll be

free. Some - day

soon, it's gon- na be_____ one day, Has

an - y - bod - y here seen my

old   friend   Bob - by?   Can   you

tell   me   where   he's   gone?_____

I thought I   saw him   walk -in'   up

o - ver   the   hill,___   with   A- bra- ham,

Mar -tin   and ___   John. _____

ACRES OF CLAMS (THE OLD SETTLERS SONG)

Words by FRANCIS D. HENRY

"The best ballad we know from the Northwest" (Lomax). Written out of the powerful fevers of the great American gold rush of 1849 by Judge Francis D. Henry, this became the state song of Washington, which entered the Union in 1889. The tune is Irish and has been used often with other lyrics such as "Lincoln and Liberty," and "Old Rosin the Beau."

I've wan-dered all o - ver this coun- try,_____ Pros-pect - ing and dig - ging for gold, _____ I've tun - neled, hy - drau - licked and cra -dled, And I have been fre - quent - ly sold, _____ And I have been fre - quent - ly sold, _____ And I have been

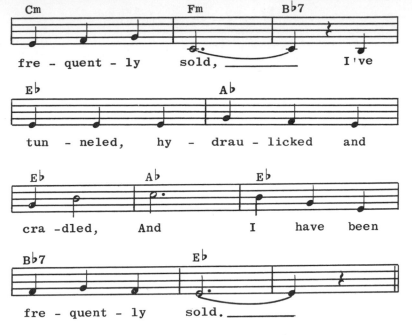

fre - quent - ly sold, _____ I've

tun - neled, hy - drau - licked and

cra -dled, And I have been

fre - quent - ly sold. _____

For one who got rich by mining
I saw there were hundreds grew poor;
I made up my mind to try farming,
The only pursuit that is sure.

The only pursuit that is sure,
The only pursuit that is sure --
I made up my mind to try farming,
The only pursuit that is sure!

I rolled up my grub in my blanket,
I left all my tools on the ground,
I started one morning to shank it
For the country they call Puget Sound.

For the country they call Puget Sound,
For the country they call Puget Sound --
I started one morning to shank it
For the country they call Puget Sound!

No longer the slave of ambition,
I laugh at the world and its shams,
And think of my happy condition
Surrounded by acres of clams.

Surrounded by acres of clams,
Surrounded by acres of clams --
And think of my happy condition
Surrounded by acres of clams.

AIN'T GONNA LET NOBODY TURN ME ROUND

A popular adaptation of an old spiritual first introduced in
Albany, Georgia, in the summer of 1962, by Rev. Ralph Aber-
nathy, during the mass arrests of Freedom Marchers there.
After the murder of Martin Luther King, Jr., Abernathy took
King's place.

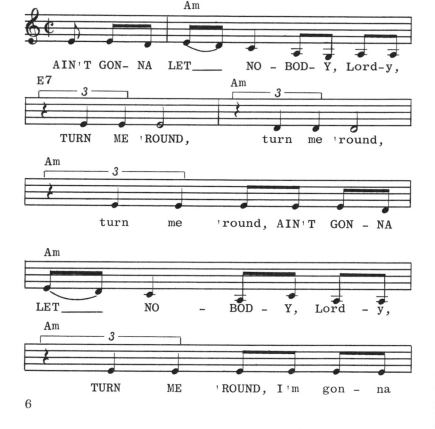

AIN'T GON-NA LET____ NO - BOD- Y, Lord-y,
TURN ME 'ROUND, turn me 'round,
turn me 'round, AIN'T GON - NA
LET____ NO - BOD - Y, Lord - y,
TURN ME 'ROUND, I'm gon - na

keep   on   a - walk - in', Lord,

Keep   on   a - talk - in', Lord,

March-ing   up   to Free-dom   Land.

Ain't gonna let Nervous Nelly turn me
    round. . .

Ain't gonna let Chief Pritchett. . .

Ain't gonna let Mayor Kelly. . .

Ain't gonna let segregation. . .

Ain't gonna let Z. T.. . .

Ain't gonna let no jail house. . .

Ain't gonna let no injunction. . .

ALL GALL

Words by MICHAEL FLANDERS; arr. by DONALD SWANN

A delicious commentary on General de Gaulle by the great team of Flanders and Swann, now dissolved, alas, though their unique material can still be heard on records.

© Michael Flanders. Used by permission.

INTRO

Fre- re Jacq -ues, Fre - re Jacq -ues,

I'm all right, I'm all right,

Son et lu-mi-er - e, son et lu- mi-er - e,

Vive De Gaulle, Vive De Gaulle.

(CHORUS)

This old man, he played one,

he played knick -knack at Ver - dun,

Cogn- ac, Ar-magn- ac, Ber-gun- dy and Beaune,

this old man came roll -ing home.

8

This old man -- World War Two
He told Churchill what to do
Free French General -- Crosses of
    Lorraine
He came rolling home again.

This old man he played TROIS
"Vive la France! La France c'est moi!
Gimcrack governments -- Call me if
    you please
Colombey les deux Eglises.

This old man he played FOUR
Choose de Gaulle or Civil War!
Come back President -- govern by
    decree
Referendum -- Oui - oui - oui!

This old man he played FIVE
"France is safe -- I'm still alive."
Plastiques, Pompidou, Sing the
    Marseilleise
ALGERIE N'EST PAS FRANCAISE.

This old man he played SIX
"France and England they don't mix
Italy, Benelux, Germany and me
That's my market recipe!"

This old man, SEVEN and EIGHT
You can count me out of NAT-O
Farewell Pentagon, find another land
Goodbye Macnamara's Band.

This old man he played NINE
"Ban the Bomb (except for mine)!"
Kiss - kiss - Moscow, Leningrad
    and all
This old man looks ten foot tall.

This old man he played TEN
He'll play Nick till Lord knows when
Cognac, Armagnac, Burgundy and Beaune,
This old man thinks he's Saint Joan!

THE ASTEROID LIGHT

Words by JOHN BOARDMAN

Appropriately enough, the words are by a young physicist, and the melody is a familiar folksong, "The Eddystone Light."

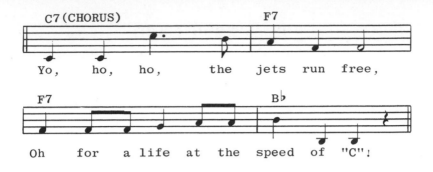

Yo, ho, ho, the jets run free,
Oh for a life at the speed of "C"!

When I was but a Space Cadet,
They put me in charge of a proton jet;
I cleaned the tubes and filled them with fuel,
And picked my teeth with an old slide rule.

One night as I was heading for the Moon
And singing a well-known spaceman's tune,
I heard a voice cry out of the void,
And there sat my mother on her asteroid.

"Oh, what has become of my children three?"
My mother then she asked of me.
"One is on exhibit in a zoo on Venus,
And the other keeps a telepathic link between us."

The deuterons flashed in her hydrogen hair;
I looked again, and my mother wasn't there.
But she telepathed angrily out of the night,
"Then to hell with the keeper
Of the ASTEROID LIGHT!"

THE BALLAD OF MOMMA ROSA PARKS

By NICK VENET and BUDDY MIZE

On December 1, 1955, Rosa Parks, a Negro seamstress, immortalized herself and set off a sociological chain reaction of monumental proportions when she suddenly refused to move to the back of a segregated bus in Montgomery, Alabama. This simple act of defiance of an age-old Southern custom catalyzed action for betterment of black conditions in an unexpected and dramatic way.

11

In Nine - teen Hun -dred and

Fif - ty Five,___ In a

south - ern A -mer- i - can town, A

tired col - ored la - dy got

on a cit - y bus and im -

me - di - ate - ly sat down, With a

closed mind ___ and an

o - pened mouth, ___ the big

bus driv - er got rough and

told his on - ly

pas - en - ger_____ to

move to the back of the bus. When

Mom - ma Parks__ sat down, the

whole world stood up, What's

good for one_____ is

good   for   all, ____   it's

good   for   all   of   us. _____

2. The lady's name was Momma Rosa Parks,
   A hard workin' woman indeed,
   She was goin' home, 'twas her goin' time,
   She had little hungry mouths to feed,
   She wasn't botherin' nobody
   And doin' nothin' wrong,
   By the Lord's rules of love
   When Momma Parks sat down
   The whole world stood up.

BALLAD OF THE TVA

Words by JILSON SETTERS

The letters TVA, in case any of the younger readers do not know, stand for the Tennessee Valley Authority, one of the more successful New Deal government projects that brought inexpensive electricity to many thousands of poor people in Kentucky and Tennessee.

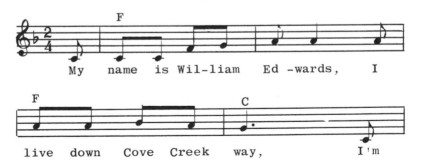

My   name   is Wil-liam   Ed -wards,   I

live   down   Cove   Creek   way,   I'm

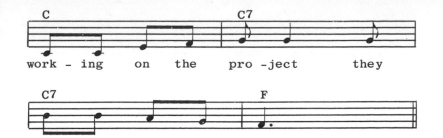

work - ing   on   the   pro -ject   they

call   the   T.   V.   A.

The Government begun it
When I was but a child,
But now they are in earnest
And Tennessee's gone wild.

Just see them boys a-comin'
Their tool kits on their arm;
They come from Clinch and Holston
And many a valley farm.

From villages and cities,
A French Broad man I see;
For things are up and doing
In sunny Tennessee.

All up and down the valley
They heard the glad alarm,
"The Government means business."
It's working like a charm.

Oh, see them boys a-comin'
Their Government they trust;
Just hear their hammers ringing
They'll build that dam or bust.

I meant to marry Sally
But work I could not find;
The T.V.A. was started
And surely eased my mind.

I'm writing her a letter
These words I'll surely say
"The Government has surely saved us,
Just name our wedding day."

We'll build a little cabin
On Cove Creek near her home;
We'll settle down forever
And never care to roam.

For things are surely movin'
Down here in Tennessee;
Good times for all the valley
For Sally and for me.

Oh, things looked blue and lonely
Until this come along;
Now hear the crew a-singin'
And listen to their song:

"The Government employs us
Short and certain pay;
Oh, things are up and comin'
God bless the T.V.A."

BAN, BAN, BAN THE BLOODY H-BOMB

Words by ALEX COMFORT

The tune is, of course, that often borrowed melody, "John Brown's Body." Dr. Alex Comfort occupies his creative time writing lyrics when he is not working at his specialty, geriatrics.

To   Hell   with all   the   hum- bug   and   to

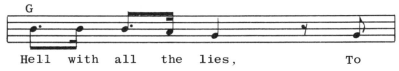

Hell   with   all   the   lies,   To

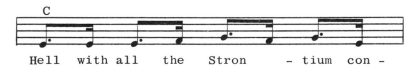

Hell   with   all   the   Stron   - tium   con -

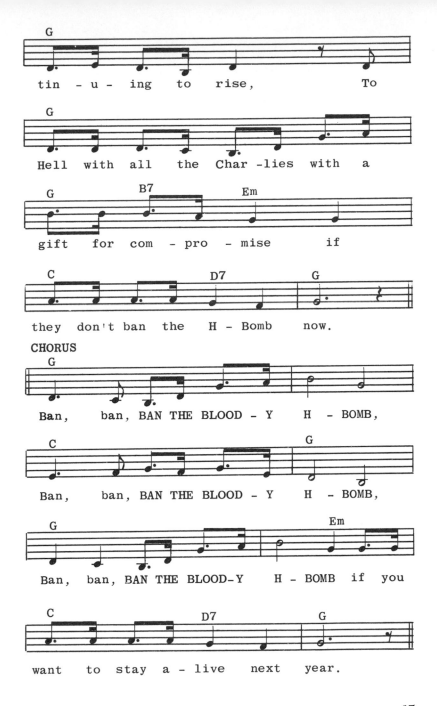

tin - u - ing to rise, To

Hell with all the Char -lies with a

gift for com - pro - mise if

they don't ban the H - Bomb now.

CHORUS

Ban, ban, BAN THE BLOOD - Y H - BOMB,

Ban, ban, BAN THE BLOOD - Y H - BOMB,

Ban, ban, BAN THE BLOOD-Y H - BOMB if you

want to stay a - live next year.

17

MacMillan and the Tories
Are out to wait and see,
They think the Great Deterrent
Will secure the victory,
I don't know if they scare the Reds,
By God! they frighten me,
If they won't ban the H-bomb now!   (CHORUS)

Gaitskell's Labour Party
Are preparing for a sell,
They want to get the votes
And keep the atom bomb as well,
But strontium will send us all
To shovel coal - in Hell -
If we don't ban the H-bomb now.   (CHORUS)

Now half of them are balmy
And half of them are blind,
They've all been talking far too long,
It's time they all resigned,
And the way to shift a donkey
Is to wallop its behind,
So we're going to ban the H-bomb now.   (CHORUS)

We're going to stop the loonies
And preserve the human race,
We're going to save our country
'Cause we love the dear old place,
We might have to stuff a rocket
Up the rocket builders' base,
But we're going to ban the H-bomb now.   (CHORUS)

Somewhere in the States
They've got a button painted red,
If anybody sits on it
We'll all of us be dead,
Meanwhile a million children
Are waiting to be fed,
So we're going to ban the H-bomb now.   (CHORUS)

BEANS, BACON AND GRAVY

A Depression protest song of uncertain authorship, but certain power.

I was born long a - go, in
Eight -een Nine - ty Four, And I've
seen man - y a pan - ic, I will
own, I've been hun -gry, I've been cold, and
now I'm grow -ing old, But the
worst I've seen is Nine- teen Thir - ty Two.

CHORUS

Oh, those BEANS, BA-CON AND GRA - VY, they
al - most drive me cra - zy, I

eat them till I see them in my

dreams (in my dreams) When I

wake up in the morn - ing, and an -

oth - er day is dawn -ing, yes, I

know I'll have an -oth - er mess of beans.

We congregate each morning
At the county barn at dawning,
And everyone is happy, so it seems;
But when our work is done
We file in one by one,
And thank the Lord for one more
    mess of beans.

We have Hooverized on butter,
For milk we've only water,
And I haven't seen a steak in many
    a day;
As for pies, cakes, and jellies,
We substitute sow-bellies,
For which we work the county road
    each day.

THE BERLIN WALL

The tune is "Joshua Fit the Battle of Jericho," and the song came out of the Freedom Movement in the 1960s in Selma, Alabama. The wall was set up by the police and was nicknamed "The Berlin Wall" by the Freedom Marchers.

From *Freedom Is a Constant Struggle,* comp. and ed. by Guy and Candie Carawan, © 1963, Oak Publications, a Div. of Embassy Music Corp., N.Y.

We're gonna break this Berlin Wall,
    Berlin Wall, Berlin Wall,
We're gonna break this Berlin Wall,
In Selma, Alabama.

We're gonna stay here 'til it fall, etc.

Hate is the thing that built that wall, etc.

Old George Wallace helped build that wall, etc.

Love is the thing that'll make it fall, etc.

We're gonna stand up 'til it fall, etc.

We've got a rope that's a Berlin Wall, etc.

BIRMINGHAM SUNDAY

Words by RICHARD FARINA

Written by the late Richard Fariña, the very talented singer-writer, once married to Joan Baez's sister, Mimi. Birmingham, of course, was the scene of several Freedom Marches and confrontations.

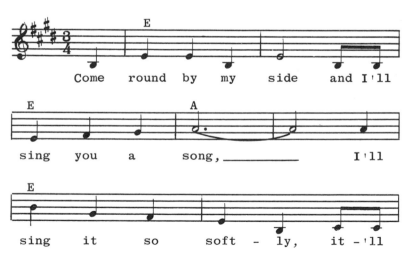

Come round by my side and I'll sing you a song, _____ I'll sing it so soft - ly, it -'ll

do no one wrong, _____ On
BIR - MING - HAM SUN - DAY the
blood ran like wine, And the
choirs _____ kept sing - ing of
Free - dom. _____

That cold autumn morning no eyes saw the sun,
And Addie Mae Collins, her number was one,
At an old Baptist church there was no need to run,
And the choirs kept singing of Freedom.

The church it was crowded, but no one could see
That Cynthia Wesley's dark number was three,
Her prayers and her feelings
Would shame you and me,
And the choirs kept singing of Freedom.

The clouds they were grey
And the autumn winds blew,
And Denise McNair brought the number to two,
The falcon of death was a creature they knew,
And the choirs kept singing of Freedom.

Young Carol Robertson entered the door
And the number her killers had given was four.
She asked for a blessing but asked for no more,
And the choirs kept singing of Freedom.

On Birmingham Sunday a noise shook the ground
And people all over the earth turned around.
For no one recalled a more cowardly sound,
And the choirs kept singing of Freedom.

The men in the forest they once asked of me,
How many black berries grew in the blue sea.
And I asked them right back with a tear in my eye,
How many dark ships in the forest?

The Sunday has come and the Sunday has gone,
And I can't do much more than to sing you a song.
I'll sing it so softly, it'll do no one wrong,
And the choirs keep singing of Freedom.

THE BLACK, BROWN AND WHITE BLUES

By BIG BILL BROONZY

One of the best songs on race ever written in this country—in
my opinion, much finer than more sophisticated efforts in the
same genre. It reminds me of a lecture I once heard by the
Negro sociologist, E. Franklin Frazier, on Brazil and its power
structure, which Frazier described as increasingly lighter
skinned as you approached the top echelons of the government,
in a country that is ninety-percent Indian and black.

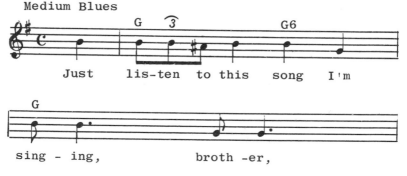

you'll know it's true,

If you're black___ and got to

work for a liv - ing, boy,___

this is what they'll say:

CHORUS

Now if you're white, you're right, and if you're

brown, _____ stick a -round, but if you're

black, _____ oh, broth- er, _____

___ git back, git back, git back.

I was in a place one night;
They was all having fun;
They was all drinking beer and wine,
But me, I couldn't buy none. (Cho.)

I was in an employment office;
I got a number and got in line.
They called everybody's number,
But they never did call mine. (Cho.)

Me and a man working side by side;
This is what it meant:
He was getting a dollar an hour,
When I was making fifty cents. (Cho.)

I helped to build this country too
I fought for it, too.
Now. . . I want to know
What you gonna do about Jim Crow? (Cho.)

BLACK EYE BLUES

A ragtime protest of an aggrieved female against her ungrieving man, which is classic in its outrage and elemental simplicity.

Down in Ho-gan's Al-ley lived Miss Nan-cy-Ann, Al-ways fuss-in', squab-blin' with her man, Then I heard Miss Nan-cy

Collected and arranged by Tom Glazer, © 1967, Songs Music, Inc., Scarborough, N.Y. All rights reserved.

say, _____ "Why do you treat your gal that

way?" I went down the Al - ley

oth -er night, Nan-cy and her man had just

had a fight,he beat Miss Nan-cy 'cross the

head, when she rose to her feet, she

said, "You low down al - li - ga -tor, just

watch me soon or lat - er, gon- na

catch you with your britch-es down. You

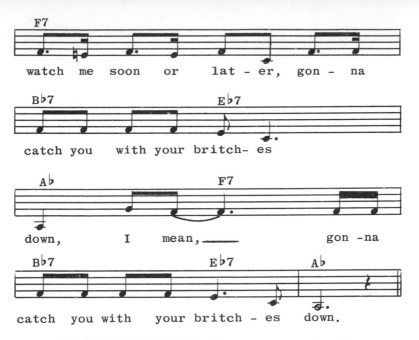

watch me soon or lat - er, gon - na

catch you with your britch- es

down, I mean,_____ gon -na

catch you with your britch - es down.

BLACK MAN FIGHTS WID DE SHOVEL

A touching, spiritual-like song of the First World War, and extremely obscure at the present time. It is ironic that the dialect poetry of, say, Robert Burns is very highly regarded, and a matter of intense Scottish racial pride, whereas black dialect poetry is, or has been regarded in quite an opposite light. The recent rise of black pride may change all that.

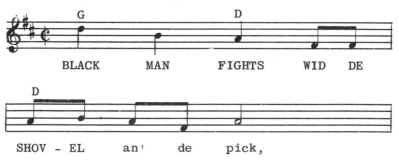

BLACK MAN FIGHTS WID DE

SHOV - EL an' de pick,

Collected and arranged by Tom Glazer, © 1967, Songs Music, Inc., Scarborough, N.Y. All rights reserved.

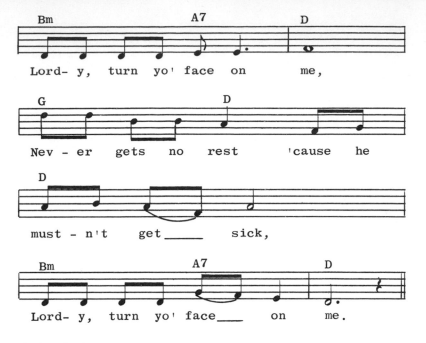

Lord- y, turn yo' face on me,

Nev - er gets no rest 'cause he

must - n't get____ sick,

Lord- y, turn yo' face____ on me.

Joined the army for to get some clothes,
Lordy, turn your face on me.
What we're fightin' about nobody knows,
Lordy, turn your face on me.

Never goin' to ride that ocean more,
Lordy, turn your face on me.
Goin' to walk right home to my cabin (front) door,
Lordy, turn your face on me.

THE BLUE DIAMOND MINES

By 'THAN HALL (Jean Ritchie)

A fine effort by Jean Ritchie, who has done so much to keep alive her white Southern Mountain folk tradition.

I re-mem-ber the ways _____ in the

by - gone ___ days, when we was all

in ____ our prime, How

us and John L., we give the

old man ___ hell, down in the BLUE

DIA - MOND ___ MINES. When the

whis-tle would blow_____ 'fore the

roost - er___ crow, full two hour be -

fore ____ day -light, When a man_

____ done his best and he____

earned his good rest and had sev- en - teen

dol-lars at night.

In the mines, in the mines, in the

BLUE DIA - MOND MINES,

I have worked my life a -

way, In the mines, in the

mines, in the BLUE DIA - MOND

MINES, _____ oh, fall on your

knees__ and __ pray.

You old black gold, you have taken my soul
Your dust has darkened my home
And now I am old, and you turn your back.
Where else can an old miner go?
It's Big Leatherwood, Algoma Block
And it's old Blue Diamond, too
Well, the pits they are closed, get another job
What work can an old miner do?

Now your union is dead, and they shake their heads
Well, minin' has had its day
But they're strippin' off my mountain top
And they pay me three dollars a day.
Oh, you might get a little poke of welfare meal
Get a little poke of welfare flour
But I tell you right now, you won't qualify
Till you work for a quarter an hour.

John L. had a dream, but it's broken it seems
Now the union's a-lettin' us down
Last night they took away my hospital card
Said, "Why don't you leave this old town?"
Well, it's go downtown and hang around
Well, maybe it ain't so bad
Go on back home and they meet you at the door
And it's "What did you bring me, Dad?"

BOOMTOWN BILL

By WOODY GUTHRIE

A lesser known (though undeservedly so) song by Woody. It harks back to the days when the oil workers were being organized by the CIO. It is doubtful that this or any song about oil will ever be popular in any on-shore towns like Santa Barbara, California, whose beaches and waters have been polluted by this coveted but trouble-making substance.

Come all you oil-field work- ers and lis - ten to my tale, I worked for Drake in Fif - ty Nine,___ 'way back in Ti - tus - ville, 'Twas the state called Penn-syl - va - nia, 'twas the

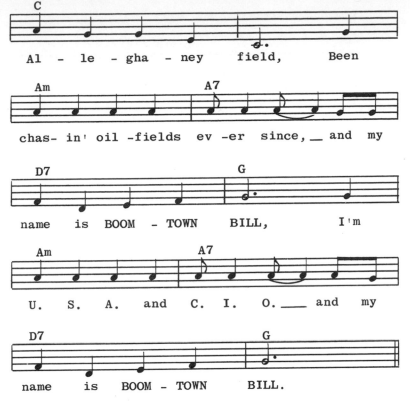

Al - le - gha - ney field, Been
chas- in' oil -fields ev -er since, __ and my
name is BOOM - TOWN BILL, I'm
U. S. A. and C. I. O. ___ and my
name is BOOM - TOWN BILL.

I held down jobs of roustybout,
Ruffneck and driller too;
Coke knocker, gauger, fireman,
And I bucked that casing crew;
Fought fires with Happy Yowell,
I'm sure you know him well;
I've worked that cross and cracking still,
And my name is BOOMTOWN BILL.

I'm a U.S.A. and C.I.O. etc.

Them walking beams and rotaries;
I know my rigs by heart;
I put your Kelly in your Rathole,
Take your Christmas Tree apart;
Gotta war ta lick them fascist rats;
This black oil's got to flow;
Best way t'beat these nazis
Is t'join the C.I.O.

I'm U.S.A. and C.I.O. etc.

I polished my bit in Texas dust;
Both these oceans and cross y'r plains;
Worked every field in forty nine states,
And I'm halfway back again;
Ten million C.I.O. workers
Just natch'lly cain't be wrong;
We'll fight and win that union way,
And I know it won't take long.

I'm U.S.A. and C.I.O. etc.

I've worked in wildest weather,
Both rain and sleet and snow,
I done all the dirty jobs,
But John Dee got my dough.
I don't know his company union,
And I know I never will;
I'm C.I.O. from head to toe,
And my name is BOOMTOWN BILL.

I'm U.S.A. and C.I.O. etc.

I lit in Oklahoma
In that boom called Seminole;
Slushed mud in Louisiana
Down along that black Bayou;
I bailed my shale from Illinois
To th' west coast Signal Hill;
Every town I go, I'm C.I.O.,
And my name is BOOMTOWN BILL.

I'm U.S.A. and C.I.O. etc.

Across this rolling ocean,
And this whole wide world around,
My union brethren and sistren
They're beatin' old race hate down;
Yes, I'm an oil field worker,
I'm a soldier in my field;
I'm-a gonna bring peace to my oil field;
Sure's my name's BOOMTOWN BILL.

I'm U.S.A. and C.I.O. etc.

BOURGEOIS BLUES

By HUDDIE LEDBETTER; edited with new additional material by ALAN LOMAX

I used to hear Leadbelly sing this at the Village Vanguard night-club in New York. It always got a laugh, but the laughs seemed somewhat embarrassed. And I used to wonder at the time how Leadbelly had latched onto the word "bourgeois," so completely out of his ethnic and rural background.

Look - a here, peo -ple, lis - ten to me, _____ don't try to find no home down in Wash - ing - ton, D. C., _____ Lord, it's a bour-geois town, __ ooh, it's a

bour-geois town, ___   I got the

BOUR - GEOIS BLUES, I'm gon - na

spread the news all ___ a -round. _____

Me and Martha was standin' upstairs,
I heard a white man say, "Don't want
   no colored up there." (Chorus)

Home of the brave, land of the free,
I don't want to be mistreated by no
   bourgeoisie. (Chorus)

White folks in Washington, they know
   how,
Throw a colored man a nickel to see
   him bow. (Chorus)

Tell all the colored folks to listen
   to me,
Don't try to find a home in Washington
   D.C. (Chorus)

BREAD AND ROSES

Words by JAMES OPPENHEIM;
music by CAROLINE KOHLSAAT

An interesting labor song of the old-fashioned type that one found especially in pre-World War I times, when the words and music of labor songs were written mainly by intellectuals. This song comes out of a famous strike in the New England textile industry around 1912. In one of the strikers' parades, a banner was carried with the words, "We want bread and roses too," which inspired the song.

As we come marching, marching,
We battle too for men,
For they are women's children,
And we mother them again.
Our lives shall not be sweated
From birth until life closes,
Hearts starve as well as bodies,
Give us bread, but give us roses

As we come marching, marching,
Unnumbered women dead
Go crying through our singing
Their ancient cry for bread.
Small art and love and beauty
Their drudging spirits knew.
Yes, it is bread we fight for--
But we fight for roses, too!

As we come marching, marching,
We bring the greater days.
The rising of the women means
The rising of the race.
No more the drudge and idler--
Ten that toil where one reposes,
But a sharing of life's glories:
Bread and roses! Bread and roses!

THE BRITISH WORKMAN'S GRAVE

What is there to say about such an eloquent lyric? It is a protest
with a vengeance, and very few protests ever live to see re-
venge. It should be sung, if possible, in its original rich Cockney accents.

They are shift-ing Dad-dy's bones to build a

sew - er, _____ They are

shift-ing them re -gard -less of ex -

pense. They are

shift -ing his re -mains just to

lay down shit -house drains To

sat - is - fy the lo - cal res - i - dents.

Now what's the use of having a religion
If after death your troubles never cease?
Just 'cause some high society twit
Wants a pipeline for his switch,
They won't let poor old daddy rest in peace!

Ah, but dad in all his life was ne'er a quitter,
And I don't think he will be a quitter now,
No, he'll dress up in his sheet
And he'll haunt that shit-house seat,
And only let them in when he'll allow.

Oh, now won't there be some pains of constipation!
And won't those high born buggers shout and writhe,
But they'll get what they deserve
For they had the bloody nerve
To desecrate a BRITISH WORKMAN'S GRAVE!

CASEY JONES

Words by JOE HILL

One of Joe Hill's most popular union songs, still sung today. It is a parody of the original Casey Jones song about a railroad engineer who perished in a train wreck. The S. P. Line refers to the Southern Pacific Railroad.

The work -ers on the S. P. line to strike sent out a call, But CAS - EY JONES, the en - gi - neer, he would-n't strike at all, His boil - er, it was leak - ing, and its driv -ers on the bum, and his

en - gine and its bear - ing, they were

all out of plumb.

CAS - EY EY JONES

kept his junk pile run - ning,

CAS - EY was

work - ing dou - ble time,

CAS - EY JONES

got a wood - en med - al for

45

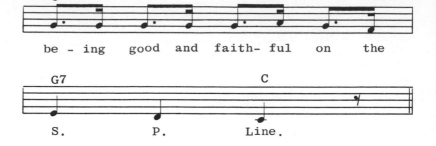

be - ing good and faith- ful on the

S. P. Line.

The workers said to Casey,
"Won't you help us win this strike?"
But Casey said, "Let me alone,
You'd better take a hike."
Then someone put a bunch of
Railroad ties across the track,
And Casey hit the river with an awful crack.

    Casey Jones hit the river bottom,
    Casey Jones broke his blooming spine,
    Casey Jones was an Angelino,
    He took a trip to Heaven on the S.P.Line.

When Casey got up to Heaven
To the Pearly Gate,
He said: "I'm Casey Jones, they guy that
Pulled the S.P. freight."
"You're just the man," said Peter,
"Our musicians are on strike.
You can get a job a-scabbing
Any time you like."

    Casey Jones got a job in Heaven,
    Casey Jones was doing mighty fine,
    Casey Jones went scabbing on the Angels
    Just like he did to workers on the S.P. Line.

The Angels got together
And they said it wasn't fair,
For Casey Jones to go around
A-scabbing everywhere.
The Angels' Union No. 23,
They sure were there,
And they promptly fired Casey
Down the Golden Stair.

```
Casey Jones went to Hell a-flying,
Casey Jones, the Devil said, "Oh fine.
Casey Jones, get busy shovelling sulphur,
That's what you get for scabbing
On the S. P. Line."
```

CERTAINLY, LORD

An adaptation of a traditional song by CORE (Congress of Racial Equality) members.

From *We Shall Overcome*, comp. by Guy and Candie Carawan, © 1963, Oak Publications, a Div. of Embassy Music Corp., N.Y. Used by permission.

CER -TAIN - LY, LORD, _____

cer -tain - ly, cer -tain - ly,

CER - TAIN - LY, LORD. ____

Well did they give you thirty days?. . .

Well did you serve your time?. . .

Well will you go back again?. . .

Well will you fight for freedom?. . .

Well will you tell it to the world?. . .

Well will you tell it to the judge?. . .

THE CLOAKMAKER'S UNION

A very funny Yiddish dialect song that has been floating around
since the early 1930s. It tells of the often bitter jealousies,
hatreds, and petty rivalries between various parties of the Left,
all of whom espoused socialism.

THE CLOAK - MAK-ER'S UN - ION is a

no good un - ion, it's a

mak - ing   by   the   work   -   ers   false

prom   -   i - ses.   They

preach   soc - ial - i - sm,   but   they

prac   -   tice fasc - i - sm   to   pre -

serve cap - 'tal- i - sm   by   the   boss-es.

COLD WAR CALYPSO

By BILL FREDERICK

Calypso has a way of almost disappearing, then suddenly becoming popular again. This has happened several times when least expected. Here is a peace song in the Calypso fashion.

50

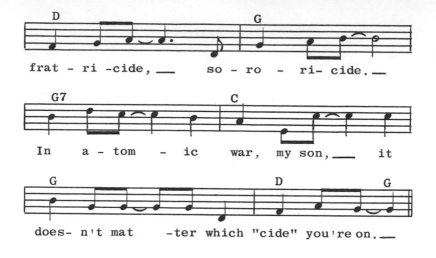

frat - ri -cide, ___ so - ro - ri- cide. ___

In a - tom - ic war, my son, ___ it

does- n't mat -ter which "cide" you're on. ___

George Washington set the colonies free,
Lincoln set the Negro free,
But now will we set the whole world free
By blowing it up in World War III?
  With patricide, matricide, there'll
  Be no place to run and hide,
  In atomic war, my son, it
  Doesn't matter which "cide" you're on.

We soon won't have to worry 'bout taxes,
The earth will be blown off its axis,
We'll have all the freedom we need then, brother,
Each molecule will be free from the other.
  And Yanks won't have to worry 'bout race,
  They'll be floating around in outer space,
  We might all die in this historic schism,
  But at least we'll prevent the spread of
  communism.

Communism will not spread,
There'll be nobody to catch it,
We laid an egg in Forty-five,
And now we're going to hatch it.
  With patricide, matricide,
  Fratricide, sororicide,
  In atomic war, my son, it
  Doesn't matter which "cide" you're on.

COLLECTOR MAN BLUES

A Depression song, interesting because it illustrates the troubles
that poor people had who did a great deal of purchasing on the
installment plan. Even insurance was, and is, sold to poor people
on the installment plan—so the collector became a likely candidate for the blues.

From *Hard Hitting Songs for Hard Hit People,* by A. Lomax, W.
Guthrie, P. Seeger, © 1947, Oak Publications, a Div. of Embassy Music
Corp., N.Y. Used by permission.

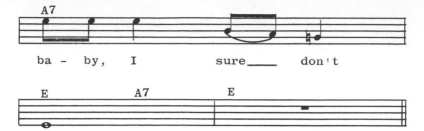

ba - by, I sure_____ don't

know.

> They will try to tear your house down, Lord,
> And this is what he will say.
> They will try to tear your house down, Lord,
> And this is what he will say:
> Says,"I've got to have some money, 'cause you
>   didn't give me nothing last pay day."
>
> Folks, one thing that I sure can't stand,
> Folks, one thing that I sure can't stand,
> Your children can't even play for hollin',
> "Daddy, here come that collector man."
>
> I've begged and borrowed til my friends don'
>   want me round,
> I'll take old man Depression and leave this
>   no good town.
>
> Depression's here, they tell me it's
>   everywhere,
> So I'm goin' back to Florida and see
>   if Depression's there.
>
> Oh, how it would help if I could just explain,
> But Depression has me, it's 'bout to drive me
>   insane.

COME AWAY, MELINDA

By FRED HELLERMAN and FRAN MINKOFF

Co-written by Fred Hellerman, a member of the famous singing group, the Weavers, now disbanded.

"Mommy, Mommy, come and see,
Oh, Mommy, come and look,
There's four or five Melinda girls
Inside this picture book."
"COME AWAY, MELINDA,
Come in and close the door,
There were lots of little girls like you
Before they had the war."

"Mommy, Mommy, come and see,
Oh, Mommy, hurry, do,
Here's someone grown up very tall
Who doesn't look like you."
"COME AWAY, MELINDA,
Come in and close the door,
Your father was a man like that
Before they had the war."

"Mommy, Mommy, come and see,
Such things I've never see,
There's happy faces all around
And all the ground is green."
"COME AWAY, MELINDA,
Come in and close the door,
That's just the way it used to be
Before they had the war."

"Mommy, Mommy, come and see,
And tell me if you can,
Why can't it be the way it was
Before the war began?"
"COME AWAY, MELINDA,
Come in and close the door,
The answer lies in yesterday,
Before they had the war."

COME BY HERE

A fraternal twin of the song "Kum-Ba-Ya" (see index).
"Wednesday I had just passed other youngsters engaged in
their game 'State Trooper,' in which half the number lined up,
locked arms, and proceeded to march, singing 'We Shall Overcome.' They were set upon and beat down by the others (children) wielding sticks and branches."—Charl Benkert, "Freedom Songs, Selma, Alabama," Folkways Records.

Slowly

COME BY HERE, my Lord, COME BY
HERE, COME BY HERE, my Lord, COME BY
HERE, COME BY HERE, my Lord, COME BY
HERE, oh, Lord,___ COME BY HERE.

Churches are burning Lord, come by here (3 times)
Oh, Lord, come by here.

Somebody's starving Lord, come by here. . .
Oh, Lord, come by here.

Somebody's shooting Lord, come by here. . .
Oh, Lord, come by here.

We want justice Lord, come by here. . .
Oh, Lord, come by here.

We want freedom Lord, come by here. . .
Oh, Lord, come by here.

COTTON MILL COLIC

Collected, Adapted, and Arranged by JOHN A. LOMAX
and ALAN LOMAX

The melody here is very much like Bob Miller's song, "Eleven
Cent Cotton," which is also in this book, and is also a song from
Depression days.

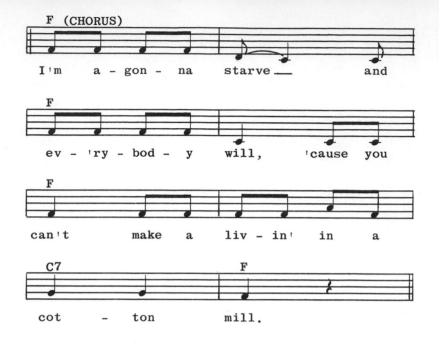

F (CHORUS)

I'm a-gon-na starve ___ and
ev-'ry-bod-y will, 'cause you
can't make a liv-in' in a
cot - ton mill.

Patches on my britches, hole in my hat,
Aint had a shave since my wife got fat.
No use to colic, we're all that way,
Can't get the money to move away.
Twelve dollars a week is all we get.
How in the hell can we live on that?
I got a wife and fourteen kids,
All we got is two bedsteads.

    I'm a-gonna starve and everybody will,
    Cause you can't make a living in a cotton mill.

When you buy clothes on Easy Terms,
Collector treats you like a measly worm.
One dollar down and then Lord knows,
If you can't make a payment they take your clothes.
When you go to bed you can't sleep,
You owe so much at the end of the week.
No use to bellyache we're all that way,
Collectors at our door til they get our pay.

    I'm a-gonna starve and everybody will,
    Cause you can't make a living in a cotton mill.

60

They run a few days and then they stand,
Just to keep down the working man.
We'll never make it, we never will,
As long as we work in a 'Rounding Mill'.
The poor getting poorer, the Rich a-getting rich,
If we don't starve, I'm a son of a bitch.
No use to bellyache, no use to rave,
We'll never rest til we're in our grave.

    If we don't starve, nobody will,
    Can't make a living in a cotton mill.

CROW ON THE CRADLE

By SIDNEY CARTER

A beautiful peace song that won second prize in a Canadian songwriting competition and was later recorded by Judy Collins.

cry for the moon and he'll

laugh at the sun, _____

If he's a boy, _____ he'll

car - ry a gun sang THE

CROW ON THE CRA - DLE.

If it should be that our baby's a girl,
Never you mind if her hair doesn't curl,
Rings on her fingers and bells on her toes,
And a bomber above her wherever she goes,
Sang THE CROW ON THE CRADLE.

Rockabye, baby, the dark and the light,
Somebody's baby is born for a fight.
Rockabye, baby, the white and the black,
Somebody's baby is not coming back,
Sang THE CROW ON THE CRADLE.

Your mammy and pappy,
They'll scrape and they'll save,
Build you a coffin and dig you a grave,
Hush-a-bye, little one, why do you weep?
We've got a toy that will put you to sleep,
Sang THE CROW ON THE CRADLE.

Bring me a gun and I'll shoot that bird dead,
That's what your mammy and pappy once said,
Crow on the cradle, oh, what shall I do?
That is a thing that I leave to you,
Sang THE CROW ON THE CRADLE.

THE CRUEL WAR IS RAGING

By PETER YARROW

An early song by Peter Yarrow of Peter, Paul and Mary, based on a folksong of the same title.

THE CRU-EL WAR IS RAG-ING,
John-ny has to fight, I
want to be with him,
morn-ing till night. _____ Today it is Sun - day,

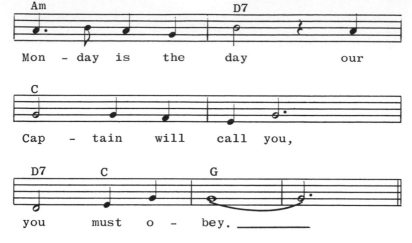

Mon - day is the day our
Cap - tain will call you,
you must o - bey. _____

Go to your Captain, get down on your knees,
Then thousand gold guineas will buy your release,
Your waist, it is slender,
Your fingers, they are small,
Your cheeks too red and rosy
To face a cannon ball.

Johnny, oh Johnny, I think you are unkind,
I love you far better than all of mankind.
I'll tie back my hair, men's clothing I'll put on,
And I'll pass as your comrade as we march along.

THE CRUEL WAR IS RAGING, Johnny has to fight,
I want to be with him from morning till night.
I want to be with him, I grieve my heart so,
If Johnny should need me, how will I know?

Across this wide country,
Around the world tonight,
My Johnny is somewhere, preparing to fight.
I love you far better than words can express,
Won't you let me go with you?
Yes, my love, yes.

CRYDERVILLE JAIL

A great jail song, one of the best, and Woody Guthrie's favorite prison song. Some of our most powerful and moving songs have come out of jails, one of the most depressing and arresting (no pun) of all human phenomena, as attested by the recent book by Dr. Karl Menninger, *The Crime of Punishment*.

Cry - der - ville Jail, no jail at all, Lice in that jail ___ are chew -in' the wall. It's HARD TIMES IN THE CRY - DER - VILLE JAIL, ___ it's hard times, ___ poor boy. ___

There's a big bull ring in the
Middle of the floor,
And a damned old jailer to open the door.

Your pockets he'll pick, your clothes he will sell
Your hands he will handcuff, goddam him to hell.

And here's to the cook, I wish he were dead,
It's old boiled beef and old corn bread.

The coffee is rough and the yards full of hogs,
And we are guarded by two bull dogs.

Our bed it is made of old rotten rugs,
And when we lay down we are covered with bugs:

The bugs they swear if we don't give bail,
We are bound to get busy in Cryderville Jail.

I wrote to my mother to send me a knife,
For the lice and the chinches
Have threatened my life.

And here's to the lawyer, he'll come to your cell,
And swear he will clear you in spite of all Hell.

Get all of your money before he will rest,
Then say, "Plead guilty, for I think it the best."

Old Judge Simpkins will read us the law,
The damndest fool judge that you ever saw.

And there sits the jury, a devil of a crew,
They'll look a poor pris'ner through and through.

And here's to the sheriff, I like to forgot,
The damndest old rascal we have in the lot.

Your privileges he will take,
Your clothes he will sell,
Get drunk on the money, goddam him to hell.

And now I have come to the end of my song,
I'll leave it to the boys as I go along.

As to gamblin' and stealin', I never shall fail,
And I don't give a damn for lying in jail.

DARK AS A DUNGEON

By MERLE TRAVIS

A great song by the author of "Sixteen Tons" (also in this book)
which has all the earmarks of a folk classic.

Come__ all you young fel-lows so young and so fine,

Seek not your for-tune in the dark drear-y mine,__ It will form like a hab-it and seep in your soul Till the stream of your blood is as black as the coal.__

67

There's many a man I have known in my day
Who lived just to labor his whole life away;
Like a fiend for his dope and a drunkard his wine,
A man will have lust for the lure of the mine.

I hope when I'm gone and the ages will roll,
My body will blacken and turn into coal;
Then I'll look from the door of my heavenly home
And pity the miner a-digging my bones.

THE DELTA BLUES

By JULIUS LESTER

A fine blues by Julius Lester, who wrote the eloquent *Blues Pilgrimage: A Mississippi Diary.*

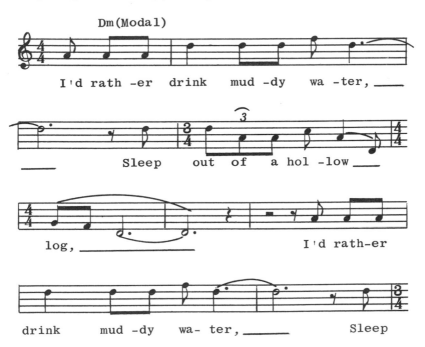

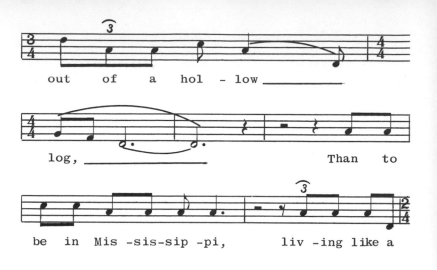

out of a hol - low _____

log, _____ Than to

be in Mis -sis-sip -pi, liv -ing like a

dirt - y dog. _____

It's down in the Delta,
Cotton up to my front door,
It's down in the Delta,
Cotton up to my front door,
And the bugs and the boss get theirs,
It ain't surprising I'm poor.

Making thirty cents an hour,
And I'm over twenty-one,
Making thirty cents an hour,
And I'm over twenty-one,
And you know my mamma told me
That my life had just begun.

Well, Mary had a baby,
But I don't believe it's mine,
Well, Mary had a baby,
But I don't believe it's mine,
Baby got blue eyes and his
Hair is just a little too fine.

(Repeat first verse)

DIE GEDANKEN SIND FREI
(THOUGHTS ARE FREE)

English lyrics by ARTHUR KEVESS

This song, dating back to the early 1800s in Hesse, Germany, was sung by German youth groups in the pre-Hitler 1930s. With recent experiments reported in the newspapers in which animals' brains are electronically controlled so as to alter emotional states, perhaps in the brave future, "die gedanken" won't be so "frei" after all.

With Student Fervor

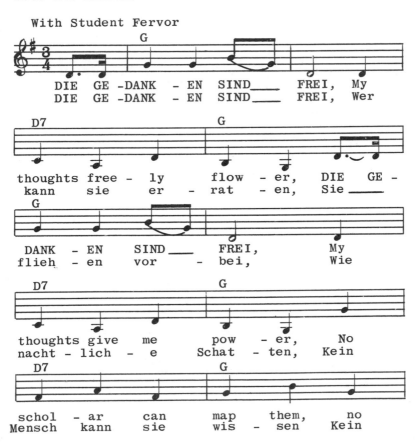

DIE GE -DANK - EN SIND___ FREI, My
DIE GE -DANK - EN SIND___ FREI, Wer

thoughts free - ly flow - er, DIE GE -
kann sie er - rat - en, Sie ___

DANK - EN SIND ___ FREI, My
flieh - en vor - bei, Wie

thoughts give me pow - er, No
nacht - lich - e Schat - ten, Kein

schol - ar can map them, no
Mensch kann sie wis - sen Kein

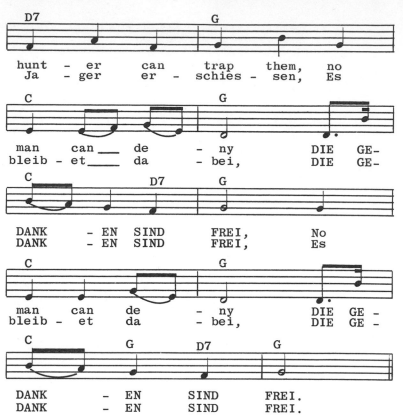

hunt - er can trap them, no
Ja - ger er - schies - sen, Es

man can ___ de - ny DIE GE-
bleib - et ___ da - bei, DIE GE-

DANK - EN SIND FREI, No
DANK - EN SIND FREI, Es

man can de - ny DIE GE -
bleib - et da - bei, DIE GE -

DANK - EN SIND FREI.
DANK - EN SIND FREI.

So I think as I please,
And this gives me pleasure;
My conscience decrees
This right I must treasure;
My thoughts will not cater
To duke or dictator;
No man can deny
Die Gedanken sind frei!
No man can deny
Die Gedanken sind frei!

Ich denke was ich will,
Und was mich beglucket,
Dock alles in der Still,
Und wie es sich schicket.
Mein Wunsch und Begehren
Kann niemand verwehren
Es bleibet dabei:
Die Gedanken sind frei!
Es bleibet dabei:
Die Gedanken sind frei!

And if tyrants take me
And throw me in prison,
My thoughts will burst free
Like blossoms in season.
Foundations will crumble,
The structure will tumble,
And free men will cry
Die Gedanken sind frei!
And free men will cry
Die Gedanken sind frei!

Und sperrt man mich ein
Im finsteren Kerker,
Das alles sind rein,
Vergebliche Werke;
Denn meine Gedanken
Zerreissen die Schranken
Und Mauern entzwei:
Die Gedanken sind frei!
Und Mauern entzwei:
Die Gedanken sind frei!

THE DODGER

Said to be linked to the campaign of Grover Cleveland in 1884,
in which the song was used satirically by his Liberal supporters
against the Republican candidate, James Blaine. It was originally collected by Charles Seeger (Pete's father) from a Mrs.
Emma Dusenberry of Arkansas.

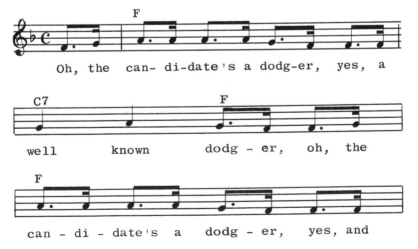

Oh, the can- di-date's a dodg-er, yes, a

well known dodg - er, oh, the

can - di - date's a dodg - er, yes, and

Oh, the lawyer's, he's a dodger,
Yes, a well-known dodger,
Oh, the lawyer, he's a dodger,
Yes, and I'm a dodger, too,
He'll plead your case
And claim you for a friend,
But look out, boys, he's easy for to bend.

Oh, the preacher, he's a dodger,
Yes, a well-known dodger,
Oh, the preacher, he's a dodger,
Yes, and I'm a dodger, too,
He'll preach you the Gospel
And tell you of your crimes,
But look out, boys, he's a-dodging for your dimes.

Oh, the merchant, he's a dodger,
Yes, a well-known dodger,
Oh, the merchant, he's a dodger,
Yes, and I'm a dodger, too,
He'll sell you goods at double the price,
And when you go to pay him
You'll have to pay him twice.

Oh, the farmer, he's a dodger,
Yes, a well-known dodger,
Oh, the farmer, he's a dodger,
Yes, and I'm a dodger, too.
He'll plow his cotton, he'll hoe his corn,
And he'll make a living
Just as sure as you're born.

Oh, the lover, he's a dodger,
Yes, a well-known dodger,
Oh, the lover, he's a dodger,
Yes, and I'm a dodger, too,
He'll hug you and kiss you and call you his bride,
But look out, girls,
He's a-telling you a lie.

A DOLLAR AIN'T A DOLLAR ANY MORE

By TOM GLAZER

I wrote this song in 1942. If a dollar wasn't a dollar any more in '42, I appeal to economists to let me know what it is (or isn't) today.

I was feel - ing kind of

hun - gry, so I thought I'd buy some

bread, and I went in - to the

cor -ner gro -c'ry store, _____ I took

out the u - sual mon - ey, but the

gro - cer shook his head, 'Cause A

DOL - LAR AIN'T A DOL - LAR AN - Y -

MORE. _____

Oh, a dol - lar bill don't buy what it used to, don't buy what it used to, don't buy what it used to, oh, a dol - lar bill don't buy what it used to 'Cause A DOL - LAR AIN'T A DOL - LAR AN - Y - MORE. _____

Now I live in a rooming house,
My room is awful small,
As a matter of fact,
It's only two by four,
Then the landlord raised the rent,
And now I'm living in the wall,
'Cause A DOLLAR AIN'T A DOLLAR ANY MORE.

From the tree that grows in Brooklyn
To the Gulf of Mexico,
From Florida out
To the Western shore,
Let's grab Congress by the collar,
"Roll those prices back," we'll holler,
'Cause A DOLLAR AIN'T A DOLLAR ANY MORE.

DONA NOBIS PACEM

One of our more popular rounds, often sung in schools and colleges and camps.

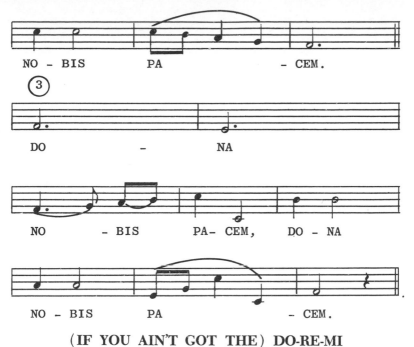

NO - BIS   PA   - CEM.

DO   -   NA

NO   - BIS   PA- CEM,   DO - NA

NO - BIS   PA   - CEM.

(IF YOU AIN'T GOT THE) DO-RE-MI

By WOODY GUTHRIE

One of Woody Guthrie's better, but more obscure, Dust Bowl ballads, telling of the trek that the Oakies and the Arkies made to the Promised Land of California during the Depression of the 1930s.

Well,   thou-sands   of   folks   back

east, they   say,   are leav - ing   home   most

ev -'ry day and they're beat-ing the hot old

dust - y way to the Cal- i -for -nia line.

Cross the des - ert sands they roll, a -

get-ting out___ of that old dust bowl and they

think they're go- ing to a sug- ar bowl,___

Here's what they find, The

po - lice at the port of en -trance

say: _____ "You're Num -ber Four - teen

E - den, _____ it's a par- a -dise to live in or see, _____ But be - lieve it or not, _____ you won't find it so hot If You Ain't Got The DO RE_____ MI. _____

Well, if you want to buy you a home or farm
That can't do nobody harm,
Or take your vacations by the mountains or the sea,
Don't swap your old cow for a car,
You'd better stay right where you are;
Well, you'd better take this little tip from me
'Cause I look through the want ads every day
And the headlines on the papers always, Oh--

Refrain

THE DOVE

Words by WALDEMAR HILLE; music by DAVID ARKIN

A poetic plea for peace through its most beautiful symbol.

DOVE makes her way un - a - fraid. _____

CHORUS

There goes THE DOVE _____ on thru the

day, _____ there goes that lit-tle bird ___

___ wing- ing her way. _____ O -ver THE

DOVE, way _____ up on

high, _____ there is a rain - bow _____

___ span -ning the sky, _____ O - ver THE

DOVE, way _____ up on

high, _____ there is a rain - bow _____

_____ span -ning the sky. _____

The rocket lights up the way,
And sears her wing with its flame,
And night burns as bright as day,
THE DOVE soars along just the same.
The guns sound off with a blast,
And snarl at THE DOVE on its course,
But there she goes faithfully past,
And braves the full burst of the force.

The people stir on the land,
They lift up their face to the sky,
To see if THE DOVE is at hand,
And watch her go breathlessly by,
The father stands with his son,
The sister and brother are there,
They lift up their heads everyone,
The sound of their voice fills the air.

The mother rich with her child,
The lover lost in her love,
To welcome the feathery, mild,
The sure, the invincible dove,
And dream of such things to be,
The wind at peace with the waves,
And the land at peace with the sea,
And the brave at peace with the brave.

DOWN BY THE RIVERSIDE

Sometimes called "I Ain't Going to Study War No More." One of the best loved spirituals and one of the strongest pleas for peace ever written in song form.

I'm gonna talk with the Prince of Peace
DOWN BY THE RIVERSIDE,
DOWN BY THE RIVERSIDE,
DOWN BY THE RIVERSIDE,
I'm gonna talk with the Prince of Peace
DOWN BY THE RIVERSIDE
I ain't gonna study war no more.

I'm gonna shake hands with every man, etc.

I'm gonna walk with my brothers in peace, etc.

I'm gonna make love, make love, not war, etc.

I'm gonna put on my freedom robe, etc.

DOWN ON ME

These are the notes of a song, carefully set down, but of such subtlety and complexity as to virtually defy accurate reproduction—proof that not all folksongs composed by uneducated people are always simple.

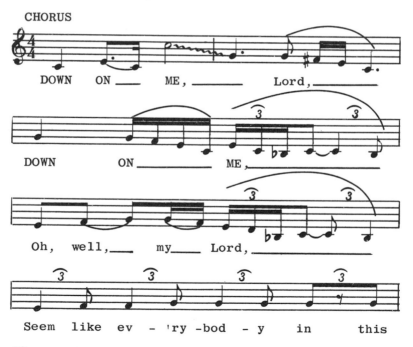

CHORUS

DOWN ON ___ ME, ___ Lord, ___

DOWN ON ___ ME, ___

Oh, well,___ my___ Lord, ___

Seem like ev - 'ry -bod - y in this

whole ___ wide world _____ is

DOWN ON ME. _____

VERSE
Won - der what Sa - tan is ___

growl - in' a - bout, _____

chained in Hell ___ and he

can't ___ get ___ out _____

Seem like ev - 'ry - bod - y in this

whole _____ wide world ___ is ___

DOWN ON ME. _____

When I get to heaven, gonna sing and shout,
Nobody there gonna put me out.
Seems like everybody in this whole wide world is
DOWN ON ME.

I've been 'buked and I've been scorned,
I've been talked about sure's you're born.
Seems like everybody in this whole wide world is
DOWN ON ME.

You can talk about me just as much as you please,
The more you talk, I'm gonna bend my knees.
Seems like everybody in this whole wide world is
DOWN ON ME.

DOWN ON PENNY'S FARM

Also known as "Robert's Farm." Bascom Lamar Lunsford, the Southern folklorist, says he learned it from a Claude Reeves of North Carolina, who claims he wrote it based on personal experience around 1935.

Come you la-dies and you gen-tle-men and

lis - ten to my song, I'll

From *Hard Hitting Songs for Hard Hit People,* by A. Lomax, W. Guthrie, P. Seeger, © 1947, Oak Publications, a Div. of Embassy Music Corp., N.Y. Used by permission.

90

sing   it   to   you   right,   but   you

might   think   it's   wrong,

may   make   you   mad,   but   I

mean   no   harm,   it's

all   a - bout   the   rent - ers   on

Pen - ny's   farm. ___

CHORUS
It's   hard   times   in   the   coun -try,

DOWN   ON   PEN- NY'S   FARM.

Now you move out on Penny's farm,
Plant a little crop of 'bacco
And a little crop of corn,
He'll come around to plan and plot,
Till he gets himself a mortgage
On everything you got.

You go to the fields and you work all day,
Till way after dark, but you get no pay,
Promise you meat or a little lard,
It's hard to be a renter on Penny's farm.

Now here's George Penny come into town,
With his wagon-load of peaches,
Not one of them sound,
He's got to have his money
Or somebody's check,
You pay him for a bushel,
And you don't get a peck.

Then George Penny's renters,
They come into town,
With their hands in their pockets
And their heads hanging down,
Go in the store and the merchant will say:
"Your mortgage is due and I'm looking for my pay."

Goes down in his pocket with a trembling hand---
"Can't pay you all but I'll pay you what I can."
Then to the telephone the merchant makes a call,
"They'll put you on the chain gang
If you don't pay it all."

DRAFT DODGER RAG

By PHIL OCHS

Phil Ochs is one of the most prolific of our topical songwriters
and probably our most bellicose lover of peace.

Moderately

I'm   just   a   typ - i - cal   A -

mer - i - can   boy   from   a

typ - i - cal   A - mer - i - can

town,   I   be - lieve   in   God   and

Sen - a - tor   Dodd   and   in

keep - ing   old   Cas - tro   down,   And

when   it   came   my   time   to   serve,   I   knew

bet - ter   dead __ than   red,   But

when   I   got   to   my   old   draft   board, bud -dy,

this　　is　　what　　I　　said:

CHORUS

Sarge, I'm　on - ly eight - een, I got a

rup - tured　spleen and　I

al - ways car- ry　a　purse,　I got

eyes　like　a　bat　and　my

feet　are　flat,　my　asth - ma's get -ting

worse,　O,　think　of　my　ca -reer, my

sweet-heart dear,　my　poor　old　in- va -lid

aunt,   be-sides I ain't no   fool, I'm a -

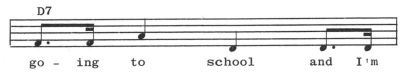

go - ing   to   school   and   I'm

work - ing in   a   de - fense plant.

I got a dislocated disc and a racked-up back,
I'm allergic to flowers and bugs,
And when the bombshell hits,
I get epileptic fits,
And I'm addicted to a thousand drugs,
I got the weakest woes
And I can't touch my toes,
I can hardly reach my knees.
And if the enemy came close to me,
I'd probably start to sneeze. (Cho.)

I hate Chou En-lai and I hope he dies,
But one thing you gotta see:
That someone's gotta go over there
And that someone isn't me.
So I wish you well,
Sarge, give 'em hell,
Yeah, kill me 'thousand or so.
And if you ever get a war
Without blood and gore,
Well, I'll be the first to go. (Cho.)

DREADFUL MEMORIES

"In 19 and 31 the Kentucky coalminers was asked to dig coal for 33¢ a ton and they had to pay the company for the carbide to make a light . . . and they had to pay for the picks and augers to be sharpened . . . and each man paid two dollars a month for the company doctor even if he did not have to call the doctor once . . . and after the miners were blacklisted for joining the union . . . the company doctor refused to come to any one of the coalminers' families unless he was paid in advance. So I had to nurse all the little children till the last breath left them, and all the light I had was a string in a can lid with a little bacon grease in it . . . thirty-seven babies died in my arms . . . they was mortified inside." (Aunt Molly Jackson)

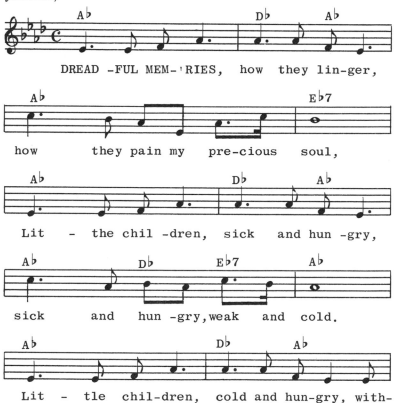

DREAD -FUL MEM-'RIES, how they lin-ger,

how they pain my pre-cious soul,

Lit - the chil -dren, sick and hun -gry,

sick and hun -gry, weak and cold.

Lit - tle chil-dren, cold and hun-gry, with-

I can't forget them, little babies,
With golden hair as soft as silk;
Slowly dying from starvation,
Their parents could not give them milk.

I can't forget them coal miners' children,
They starved to death without one drop of milk,
While the coal operators
And their wives and children
Were all dressed in jewels and silk.

CHORUS:
Dreadful memories! How they haunt me
As the lonely moments fly.
Oh, how them little babies suffered!
I saw them starve to death and die.

DRILL, YE TARRIERS, DRILL

According to some, tarriers were so called because the Irish
railroad workers here wore beards, and the word was supposed
to be a take-off on the word "terrier," but I am assured that "tar-
rier" simply means one who tarries, and was used to goad the
Irish Eastern railroad workers to work faster in competition
with the Western railroad workers during the construction of
the first transcontinental railroad.

Ev - 'ry morn -in' at

sev - en o' - clock, there were

twen - ty tar - ri - ers a -

drill -in' on the rock, and the

boss comes a-round and he says,"Keep still,

come down heav - y on the cast i-ron drill,"

CHORUS

And DRILL, YE TAR - RI -ERS,

drill, and DRILL, YE TAR - RI - ERS,

drill, For it's work all day for

sug - ar in your tay, down be - hind the

rail -way, and DRILL, YE TAR- RI -ERS,

drill and blast and fire!"

The new foreman was Jean McCann
By God he was a blamed mean man
Last week a premature blast went off
And a mile in the air went big Jim Goff.

When next payday it came around,
Jim Goff a dollar short was found,
When he asked what for, came this reply:
"You were docked for the time
You were up in the sky."

The cook was a fine man down to the ground
He married a lady six foot around
She baked good cakes and she baked them well
But she baked them harder than the holes in hell.

DUST PNEUMONIA BLUES

Words and new music adaptation by WOODY GUTHRIE

The title is Woody Guthrie's phrase, I suppose, to describe silicosis, the debilitating and fatal disease that attacked certain miners in the 1930s.

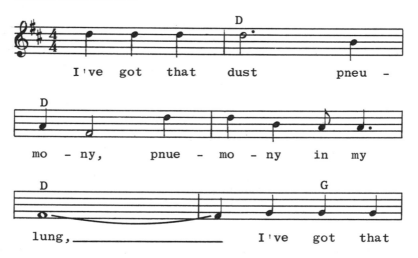

dust pnue - mo - ny, pnue - mo - ny in my lung, and I'm gon - na sing this dust pnue - mo - ny song.

I went to the doctor
And the doctor said, my son,
Yes, I went to the doctor
And the doctor said, my son,
You got that dust pnuemony
And you ain't got long, not long.

Now there ought to be
Some yodelling in this song,
There ought to be
Some yodelling in this song,
But I can't yodel
For the rattling in my lung.

My good girl sings
THE DUST PNUEMONY BLUES,
My good girl sings
THE DUST PNUEMONY BLUES,
She loves me 'cause she's
Got the dust pnuemony too.

If it wasn't for choppin,
My ax would turn to rust,
If it wasn't for choppin,
My ax would turn to rust,
I can't find a woman in this
Black old Texas dust.

Down in Oklahoma
The wind blows mighty strong,
Down in Oklahoma
The wind blows mighty strong,
If you want to get in, mam,
Just sing a California song.

Down in Texas,
My gal fainted in the rain,
Down in Texas,
My gal fainted in the rain,
I throwed a bucket o' dirt in her face
Just to bring her back again.

ELEVEN CENT COTTON

By BOB MILLER and EMMA DERMER

One can tell from the prices mentioned in this song of the 1920s and 1930s how far prices have advanced in our inflationary times. Even in the midst of our affluence, studies show that there is still plenty of hunger in the United States, so that no matter what the price is, "How in the hell can a poor man eat?"

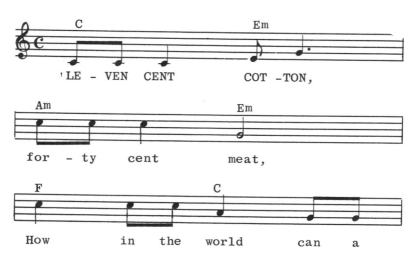

poor man eat? Pray for the sun- shine,

'cause it will rain,

things get - tin' worse, driv - in'

us in - sane. Built a nice house,

paint - ed it brown,

light - nin' came a - long and

burnt it down, No use talk - in',

an - y man's beat with

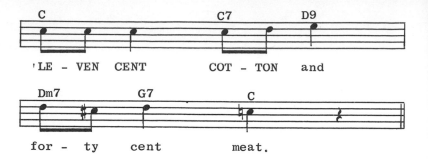

'LE - VEN CENT COT - TON and

for - ty cent meat.

'Leven-cent cotton, forty-cent meat,
Keep gettin' thinner 'cause we don't eat;
Tried to raise peas, tried to raise beans;
All we can raise is turnip greens.
No corn in the crib, no chicks in the yard,
No meat in the smoke house, no tubs full of lard;
No use talkin', any man's beat
With 'leven-cent cotton and forty-cent meat.

'Leven-cent cotton, forty-cent meat,
How in the world can a poor man eat?
Our clothes worn out, shoes run down,
Old slouch hat with a hole in the crown.
Poor gettin' poorer all around here,
Kids comin' regular ev'ry year;
No use talkin', any man's beat
With 'leven-cent cotton and forty-cent meat.

'Leven-cent cotton, forty-cent meat,
How in the world can a poor man eat?
Mule's in the barn, no crop's laid by,
Corn crib empty and the cow's gone dry.
Well water's low, nearly out of sight,
Can't take a bath on a Saturday night.
No use talkin', any man's beat
With 'leven-cent cotton and forty-cent meat.

EN ESPANA LAS FLORES

This is one of two songs in this book (the other being "La Mujer de Pancho Franco") that I ran across in Paris in 1964 in a book published in France and in Italy, called "Songs of the New Spanish Resistance."

From *Chansons de la nouvelle résistance espagnole*, Paris, 1963, ©
1962, Enaudi Editore, Torino. Used by permission.

EN ES- PA- ÑA LAS FLO - RES,

que na -cen en a - bril, ____

Por-que el pue -blo es- pa - nol, ____

mu -rio en a - bril, ____

Pe - ro las flo - res vuel - ven

Quien las hi - zo mo - rir. ____

En Espana, las flores
que nacen en abril,
no nacen de alegria,
si de dolores, si.

De tres años de tiros,
de tres años, y mil
que resistió su pueblo
solo contra el fusil.

En Espana, la flores
no quieren ya vivir.
Porque el pueblo espanol
murió en abril.

Pero las flores vuelven.
Quien las hizo morir
no sabe que las flores
vuelven en cada abril.

Espana nunca ha muerto
nunca puede morir.
Al pueblo y a la flor
no los mata el fusil.

TRANSLATION:

In Spain the flowers which are born in April
Are not born in happiness, but full of sorrows.

For three years of combat,
For three years and a thousand
When her people resisted alone against the gun.

In Spain the flowers do not wish to live any more,
For the Spanish people died in April,
But the flowers will return.
He who killed them doesn't know
The flowers come back every April.
Spain has never dies, it never can die,
The gun can kill neither people
Nor the flower.

EVERYBODY WANTS FREEDOM

This comparatively recent freedom song has the same melody
as the spiritual "Amen," which was done so effectively by Sidney Poitier in his film *Lilies of the Field*.

(Tune: "AMEN")

FREE   -   DOM,   FREE   -

DOM,   FREE   -   DOM.

CHORUS

Ev - 'ry- bod - y wants   FREE   -

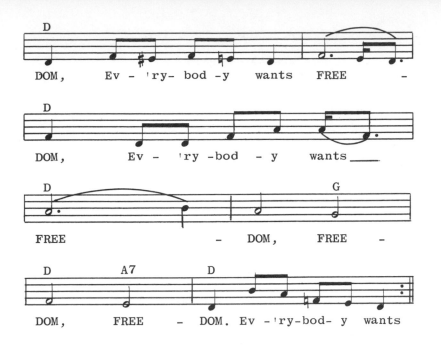

DOM, Ev - 'ry- bod -y wants FREE -

DOM, Ev - 'ry -bod - y wants ____

FREE - DOM, FREE -

DOM, FREE - DOM. Ev -'ry-bod- y wants

THE FARMER

From the earliest days of our country, when it was more agrarian than industrial, farmers' troubles were long and loud. Of all farmers' protest songs, this is one of the most outstanding. It originated just after the Civil War, and was picked up once by Carl Sandburg from a milkman in Galesburg, Illinois, a reformed country fiddler.

With a Lilt

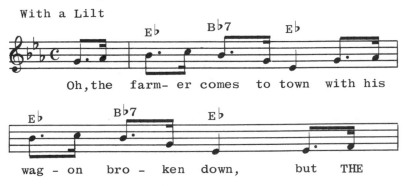

Oh, the farm- er comes to town with his

wag - on bro - ken down, but THE

FARM - ER IS THE MAN who feeds them

all, If you'll

on - ly look and see, I _____

think you will a - gree that THE

FARM- ER IS THE MAN who feeds them all.

CHORUS

THE FARM - ER IS THE MAN, THE

FARM - ER IS THE MAN,

lives on cred- it till the fall, then they

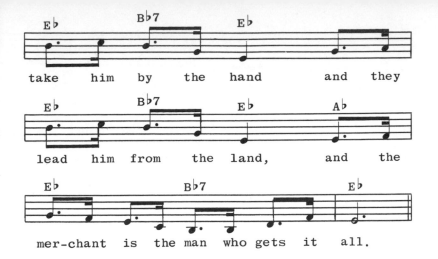

take him by the hand and they
lead him from the land, and the
mer-chant is the man who gets it all.

When the lawyer hangs around
While the butcher cuts a pound,
Oh, the farmer is the man who
     feeds them all
When the preacher and the cook
Go a-strolling by the brook,
Oh, the farmer is the man who
     feeds them all,

When the banker says he's broke
And the merchant's up in smoke,
They forget that it's the farmer
     feeds them all.
It would put them to the test
If the farmer took a rest;
Then they'd know that it's the
     farmer feeds them all.

LAST CHORUS:
     The farmer is the man,
     The farmer is the man,
     Lives on credit till the fall --
     With the interest rate so high
     It's a wonder he don't die,
     For the mortgage man's the one
          who got it all.

FIGHTING FOR MY RIGHTS

Words by CHARLES NEBLETT and CHARLES WINGFIELD;
music by DOC POMUS

The tune is from a popular modern song called "Lonely Avenue" by Doc Pomus. It was adapted with new freedom words during the Freedom Movement of the 1960s.

You know I'm tired of se-gre-ga-tion, and I want my e - qual rights, __ Se - gre-ga - tion did me wrong, __ made me leave my hap - py home, __ That's why I'm FIGHT - ING FOR MY RIGHTS,

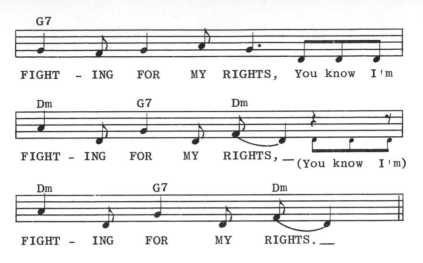

FIGHT - ING FOR MY RIGHTS, You know I'm

FIGHT - ING FOR MY RIGHTS, — (You know I'm)

FIGHT - ING FOR MY RIGHTS. —

My mother, yeah, she told me
On her dying bed,
Son, if you don't get your freedom
You know I'd rather see you dead.

Well my father, yes, he told me
A long, long time ago
Son, if you don't fight for freedom
You'll be a slave forever more.

Well-a I want my freedom
And I want it now
And no matter what happens
I'm gonna fight on anyhow.

Well my cell it had two windows
But the sun could never come through
And I felt so sad and lonely
You know I didn't know what to do.

Well an old lady told me
And she was very brave
She said before she'll be a slave
She'd be buried in her grave.

111

FOLLOW THE DRINKIN' GOURD

By PAUL CAMPBELL

Based on a traditional Underground Railway song. The "drinking gourd" is supposed to be the Big Dipper, which points North and consequently to freedom.

FOL- LOW _____ THE DRINK - IN' GOURD, __ FOL- LOW _____ THE DRINK - IN' GOURD, __ For the old man is a - wait - in' for to car - ry you to free - dom, FOL -LOW THE DRINK - IN' GOURD.

When the sun comes back and the first quail calls, ____ FOL - LOW THE DRINK -IN' GOURD, __ The old man is a - wait - in' for to car - ry you to free - dom, FOL -LOW THE DRINK - IN' GOURD.

2. Now the river bank'll make a mighty good road,
   The dead trees will show you the way.
   Left foot, peg foot, travelin' on,
   FOLLOW THE DRINKIN' GOURD. (Chorus)

3. Now the river ends between two hills,
   FOLLOW THE DRINKIN' GOURD.
   There's another river on the other side,
   FOLLOW THE DRINKIN' GOURD. (Chorus)

FREE AT LAST

Martin Luther King Jr.'s favorite spiritual was quoted in his famous speech, which ended, "This will be the time when all of God's children—black and white men; Jews and Gentiles; Protestants and Catholics—will be able to join hands and sing in the words of the old Negro spiritual, 'Free at last! Free at last! Thank God Almighty! We are free at last!' "

CHORUS

FREE AT LAST! FREE AT LAST! ____

Thank God a' - might - y, I'm

FREE AT LAST! ____

FREE AT LAST! FREE AT LAST! ____

Thank God a'-might-y, I'm FREE AT LAST!

One of these morn-ings bright and fair,

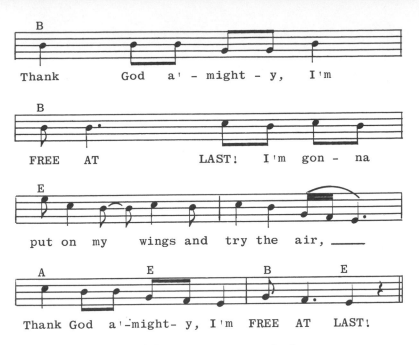

Thank God a'-might-y, I'm FREE AT LAST! I'm gon-na put on my wings and try the air, ____ Thank God a'-might-y, I'm FREE AT LAST!

Old Satan's mad because we're glad,
Thank God Almighty, we're free at last!
He missed a crowd he thought he had,
Thank God Almighty, we're free at last!

I wonder what old Satan's grumblin 'bout
Thank God Almighty, we're free at last!
'Cause he's chained in hell, and can't get out,
Thank God Almighty, we're free at last!

FREEDOM IS A CONSTANT STRUGGLE

By ROBERTA SLAVIT

Written, says the writer, "on a picket line in Virginia, in 1963."
The tune is somewhat similar to the famous white spiritual,
"Wayfaring Stranger."

we must___ be free, we must be free.

They say that freedom is a constant crying,
They say that freedom is a constant crying,
They say that freedom is a constant crying,
Oh Lord, we've cried so long,
We must be free, we must be free.

They say that freedom is a constant sorrow . . .
Oh Lord, we've sorrowed so long . . .

They say that freedom is a constant moaning . . .
Oh Lord, we've moaned so long . . .

They say that freedom is a constant dying . . .
O Lord, we've died so long,
We must be free, we must be free.

FREEDOM'S COMIN' AND IT WON'T BE LONG

Some members of CORE wrote this song during the violence
launched against the Freedom Strikers in the South of the 1960s.

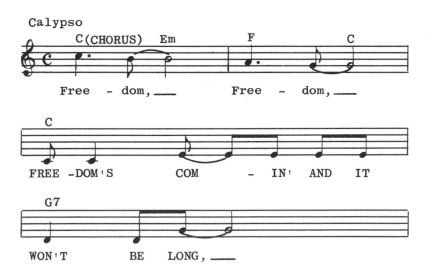

Free - dom, _____ Free - dom, _____

FREE -DOM'S COM - IN' AND IT

WON'T BE LONG. _____

Took a trip _____ down Al - a -

ba - ma way, _____

FREE - DOM'S COM - IN' AND IT

WON'T BE LONG, _____

Met much vi - o - lence on

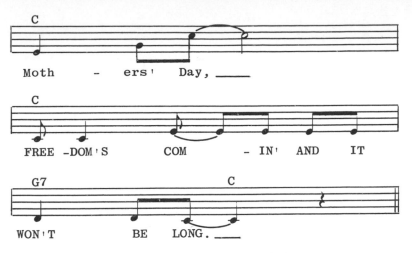

Moth - ers' Day, ____

FREE -DOM'S COM - IN' AND IT

WON'T BE LONG. ____

We took a trip on a Greyhound bus,
Freedom's comin' and it won't be long
To fight segregation, this we must
Freedom's comin' and it won't be long.

Violence in 'bama didn't stop our cause
Freedom's comin' and it won't be long
Federal marshals come enforce the laws
Freedom's comin' and it won't be long.

On to Mississippi with speed we go
Freedom's comin' and it won't be long
Blue-shirted policemen meet us at the door
Freedom's comin' and it won't be long.

Judge say local custom shall prevail
Freedom's comin' and it won't be long
We say 'no' and we land in jail
Freedom's comin' and it won't be long.

FREIHEIT

Words by KARL ERNST; music by PETER DANIEL

Written by German soldiers of the International Brigade during
the Spanish Civil War in 1936. It is undoubtedly one of the
most stirring songs of its kind ever written. Its final two notes,
to which the word "Freiheit" is half-sung, half-shouted, are
positively bloodcurdling.

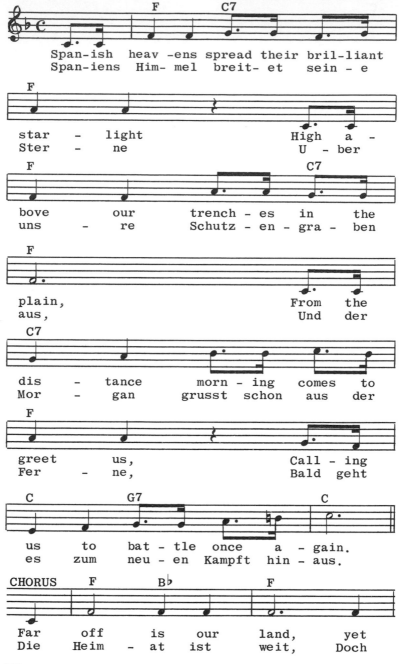

Span-ish heav-ens spread their bril-liant
Span-iens Him-mel breit-et sein-e

star - light
Ster - ne

High a -
U - ber

bove our trench-es in the
uns - re Schutz-en-gra-ben

plain, From the
aus, Und der

dis - tance morn-ing comes to
Mor - gan grusst schon aus der

greet us, Call-ing
Fer - ne, Bald geht

us to bat-tle once a - gain.
es zum neu-en Kampft hin-aus.

CHORUS

Far off is our land, yet
Die Heim - at ist weit, Doch

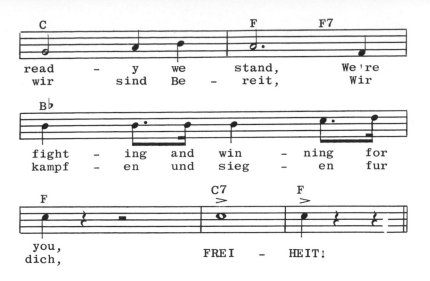

We'll not yield a foot to Franco's fascists,
Even though the bullets fall like sleet,
With us stand those peerless men, our comrades,
And for us there can be no retreat.

Dem Faschisten werden wir nicht weichen,
Schickt er auch die Kugeln hageldicht.
Mit uns stehn Kameraden ohne gleichen
Und ein Ruckwarts gibt es für uns nicht.

FURUSATO

By ISHIGI ASTU

A Japanese anti-atom bomb song with English lyrics attributed
to Ewen MacColl, the well-known Scottish singer-songwriter.

Deadly rain gathers poison from the sky,
And the fish carry death
In the depths of the sea,
Fishing boats are idle,their owners are blind,
Deadly harvest of two atom bombs.
Then landsmen and seamen,
You must watch and take care
That the third atom bomb never comes.

Furusato no umi arete
Kuroki ame yorokobino hiwanaku
Imawa fu ne ni hito mo-na si
Ah . . . yurusu maji genbaku-o
Mitabi yurusu maji genbaku-o
Warera no umini.

Hara karano taye manaki
Rodoni kizuki agu tomito saiwai
Imawa subete tsuiye saran
Ahyurusu maji genbakuo
Mitabi yurusu maji genbakuo
Sekai no uyeni.

GEE, MOM, I WANT TO GO HOME
(I DON'T WANT NO MORE OF ARMY LIFE)

By ESTHER VAN SCIVER and SHELBY DARNELL

Very popular during World War II, its exact origin is obscure.
This version is probably an adaptation of a song of that period
that was just kind of floating around.

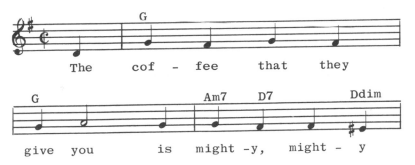

The cof - fee that they give you is might -y, might - y

The bisquits that they serve you
Are very, very fine,
One fell right off the table
And killed a pal of mine.

The uniforms they give you
Are tailor-made to fit,
The blouse fits like a hopsack,
The pants so tight, they split.

The sergeant, he's a fine one,
We've never seen him drunk,
But under all his fancy stripes,
At heart he is a skunk.

The girls we never get to see,
We miss 'em very much,
You just can't substitute for dames
With movies, dreams and such.

GET ON BOARD, LITTLE CHILDREN

An adaptation of a famous spiritual used in Mississippi by members of SNCC during the difficult days of the Freedom Strikers in the 1960s.

GET ON BOARD, LIT - TLE

CHIL -DREN, GET ON BOARD, LIT - TLE

CHIL -DREN, GET ON BOARD, LIT - TLE

CHIL -DREN, let's fight for hu-man rights.

I hear those mobs a - howl - ing and

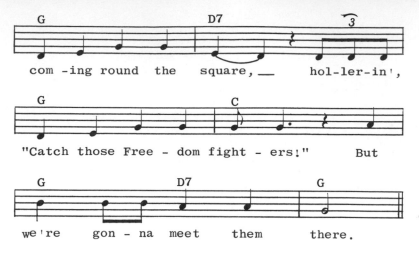

com -ing round the square, ___ hol-ler-in',

"Catch those Free - dom fight - ers!" But

we're gon - na meet them there.

As fighters we're not running
For we are here to stay
Forget about Ross Barnett
The Lord will make a way.

As fighters we're aware of the fact
That we may go to jail
But if you fight for freedom,
There's no such thing as bail.

As fighters we go hungry,
Sometimes don't sleep or eat
We're gonna keep on fighting for freedom,
In the end we will be free.

Can't you see that mob a' comin',
Comin' 'round the bend,
If you fight for freedom,
They sure will let you in.

GET THEE BEHIND ME, SATAN

By PETE SEEGER, LEE HAYS, and MILLARD LAMPELL

Made famous by the Almanac Singers, who originally sang it
for striking auto workers in Detroit in 1941. Most of it was
written by Lee Hays, and some of it by Pete Seeger and Millard
Lampell.

Blues Style

The boss comes up to me with a

five dol - lar bill, ___ Says,

"Get you some whis -key, boy, and

drink your fill."

CHORUS

GET THEE BE - HIND ME, SA - TAN,

trav -el on down the line, ___

I am a un - ion man, ___

gon-na leave ___ you be- hind. _____

A red-headed woman took me out to dine,
Says, "Love me, baby, leave your union behind."

On the Fourth of July the politicians say:
"Vote for us, and we will raise your pay."

Oh, then the company union sent out a call,
Said, "Join us in the summer,
We'll forget you in the fall."

If anyone should ask you your union to sell,
Just tell him where to go, send him back to Hell.

GO DOWN, MOSES

The never-aging spiritual, for slaves of yore and today; for near-slaves and prisoners of all kinds, times, and places.

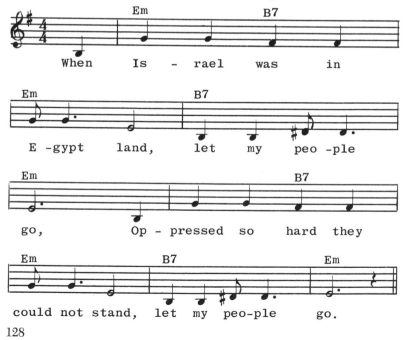

steal your nu -clear se - crets you'll

wish you were dead.

CHORUS

Sing -ing too - ra - li, oo - ra - li,

oo - ra - li - ay.

O mother, dear mother, I am not afraid,
For I'll go on that march and I'll return a maid,
With a brick in my handbag and a scowl on my face,
And barbed wire in my underwear to head off
    disgrace.

But as they were marching, a young man came by,
With a beard on his chin and a gleam in his eye,
And before she had time to remember her brick,
They were holding a sitdown on a neighboring
    hayrick.

Now once at the briefing, she'd heard a man say,
"Go perfectly limp and be carried away."
So when this chap suggested it was time she was
    kissed,
She remembered her briefing and did not resist.

O meeting is pleasure and parting is pain,
I don't need to sing all that folk stuff again,
O mother, O mother, I'm stiff and I'm sore
I'm sleeping three nights on a hard classroom
    floor.

THE GOOD BOY

A Carl Sandburg find from a New York newspaperman named
Lem Parton. It was unforgettable to hear Sandburg sing this
song in his throaty, effortless, Midwestern-Scandinavian voice,
and it remains the most irreverent protest song against Estab-
lishment values ever written.

have an old age, ri - bald,

coarse and blood - y. _____

I have led a good life, full of peace and quiet,
I shall have an old age full of rum and riot;
I have been a good boy, wed to peace and study,
I shall have an old age, ribald, coarse and bloody.

I have never cut throats, even when I yearned to,
Never sang dirty songs that my fancy turned to;
I have been a nice boy and done what was expected,
I shall be an old bum loved but unrespected.

GO TELL IT ON THE MOUNTAIN

A Freedom Movement adaptation of the famous old spiritual.

CHORUS

GO TELL IT ON THE MOUN - TAIN,

o -ver the hills and ev -'ry -where,

GO TELL IT ON THE MOUN - TAIN to

let my peo - ple go!

O, Paul and Si -las bound __ in jail,

Let my peo -ple go! O,

had no mon -ey to go their bail,

Let my peo - ple go!

Who's that yonder dressed in red?
Let my people go,
It must be the children Bob Moses
  led,
Let my people go.

Who's that yonder dressed in black?
Let my people go,
It must be the Uncle Toms turning
  back,
Let my people go.

Who's that yonder dressed in blue?
Let my people go,
It must be the registrars coming
  through,
Let my people go.

Birmingham version:

CHORUS:
GO TELL IT ON THE MOUNTAIN, over the
    hills and everywhere,
GO TELL IT ON THE MOUNTAIN, that
    freedom is coming soon. Halleluia.

You know I would not be Governor
    Wallace,
I'll tell you the reason why,
I'd be afraid the Lord might call me
And I would not be ready to die.

Oh I would not be Mayor Boutwell, etc.

Oh I would not be Barry Goldwater, etc.

Oh I would not be the segregationists, etc.

HALLELUJAH, I'M A-TRAVELIN'

By HARRY RICHMOND

An interesting example of the metamorphosis of one single tune, first from a hymn called "Hallelujah,, Thine the Glory," to the hobo song, "Hallelujah, I'm a Bum" (possibly written by Harry McClintock, an old IWW member), to an early bus-integration song, "Hallelujah, I'm A-Travelin'."

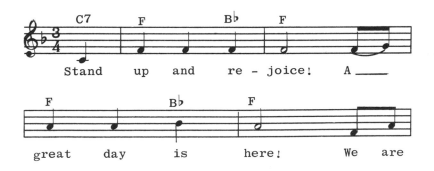

fight - ing   Jim   Crow   and   the
vic - t'ry   is____   near.
HAL- LE - LU - JAH,   I'M   A -
TRAV- EL -IN', Hal -le - lu - jah, ain't it
fine?   HAL - LE - LU - JAH,   I'M   A -
TRAV -EL - IN'   down free -dom's main   line.

I read in the news,
The Supreme Court said,
"Listen here, Mister Jim Crow,
It's time you was dead."

The Judges declared
In Washington town,
"You white folks must take that
Old Jim Crow sign down."

I'm paying my fare
On the Greyhound Bus line,
I'm riding the front seat
To Nashville this time.

Columbia's the gem of the ocean,
They say,
We're fighting Jim Crow
In Columbia today.

I hate Jim Crow
And Jim Crow hates me,
And that's why I'm fighting
For my liberty.

HARD TIME BLUES

Words by W. W. CUNEY; music by JOSH WHITE

One of Josh White's rare original songs. It is important because
it was one of the first Depression folksongs to make a tremendous impression in the big cities in the 1930s by way of one of
Josh's first recordings.

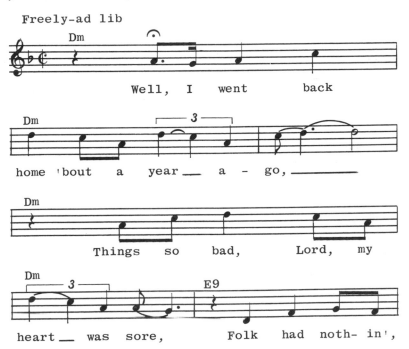

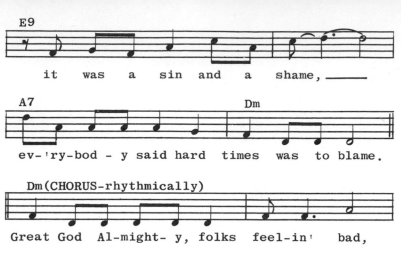

it was a sin and a shame, _____

ev-'ry-bod - y said hard times was to blame.

Great God Al-might- y, folks feel-in' bad,

lost ev -'ry-thing I ev - er had,

Great God Al-might- y, folks feel -in' bad,

lost ev -'ry-thing I ev - er had.

Now the sun was a-shinin'
Fourteen days and no rain,
They had hard times, hard times, Lord, all around
Meal barrels empty, crops burned to the ground.

They had skinny lookin' children,
Bellies pokin' out,
That old pellagra without a doubt
Old folks hangin' round the cabin door
Ain't seen times this hard before.

Well, I went to the boss at the commissary store
"Folks all starvin', Please don't close your door,
We want more food and a little more time to pay."
Boss man laughed and walked away.

HARD TIMES IN THE MILL

The textile industry in this country has had more than its share of bitter struggles between workers and management. In the 1930s, for example, almost half a million workers struck mills all over the countryside, and thousands were blacklisted for their pains, while in one year alone twenty workers were relieved of *their* pains by being killed. "Hard Times in the Mill" is based on "Cryderville Jail" and came out of the Columbia Duck Mills, Columbia, South Carolina, in the early 1900s.

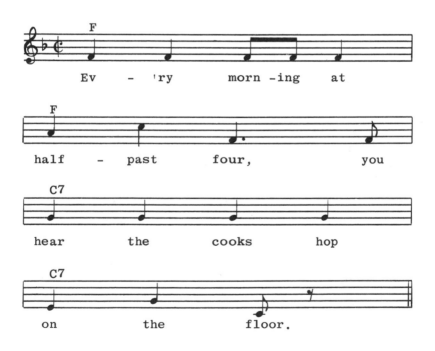

IT'S HARD TIMES IN THE MILL, my love,

HARD TIMES IN THE MILL.

Every morning just at five
You gotta get up, dead or alive.

Every morning at six o'clock
Two cold biscuits, hard as a rock.

Every morning at half-past nine
The bosses are cussin' and the spinners are cryin'.

They docked me a nickel, they docked me a dime,
They sent me to the office to get my time.

Cotton mill boys don't make enough
To buy them tobacco and a box of snuff.

Every night when I get home,
A piece of corn bread and an old jawbone.

Ain't it enough to break your heart?
Hafta work all day and at night it's dark.

HE WAS A FRIEND OF MINE

By BOB DYLAN

One of Bob Dylan's early songs, while he was still very much
under the influence of Woody Guthrie and folksongs in general.
Although not directly concerned with peace, freedom, or protest, it is an interesting expression, through a strong feeling
for a "buddy" in particular, of brotherhood in general.

HE _____ WAS A FRIEND OF MINE,
He _____
____ WAS A FRIEND OF MINE, ____
Ev-'ry time I think a -bout him
now, Lord, I just can't keep from cryin'
____ 'cause HE _____
____ WAS A FRIEND OF MINE. ____

He died on the road,
He died on the road,
He never had enough money
To pay his room or board,
And he was a friend of mine.

143

I stole away and cried,
I stole away and cried,
'Cause I never had too much money,
And I never been quite satisfied,
And he was a friend of mine.

He never done no wrong,
He never done no wrong,
A thousand miles from home,
And he never harmed no-one,
And he was a friend of mine.

He was a friend of mine,
He was a friend of mine,
Ev'ry time I hear his name,
Well, I just can't keep from cry'n',
'Cause he was a friend of mine.

HE WAS MY BROTHER

By PAUL KANE (Paul Simon)

Written by Paul Kane, who now goes under his real name of
Paul Simon, who sings with a man named Art Garfunkel, who
are widely known as Simon and Garfunkel.

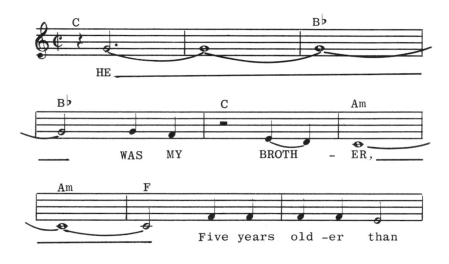

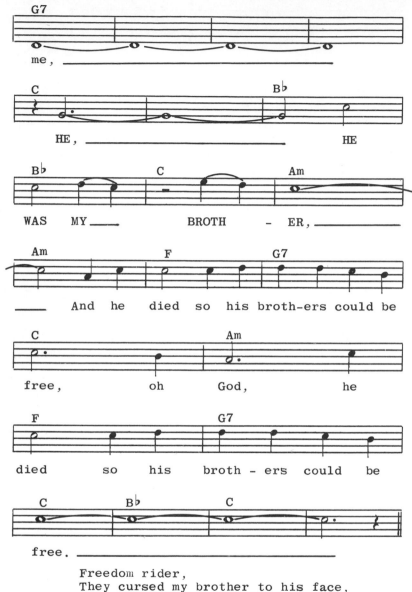

Freedom rider,
They cursed my brother to his face,
"Go home, outsider, this town's
Gonna be your buryin' place."

He was singin' on his knees,
An angry mob trailed along,
They shot my brother dead
Because he hated what was wrong.

HOLD UP YOUR LIGHT

A take-off on the spiritual "Heaven Bound Soldier." The melody is an unusually moving one, and the words, which seem somewhat old-fashioned today, vividly illustrate the serious and affectionate interest in the Negro by forward-looking men of good will. The song deserves to be better known.

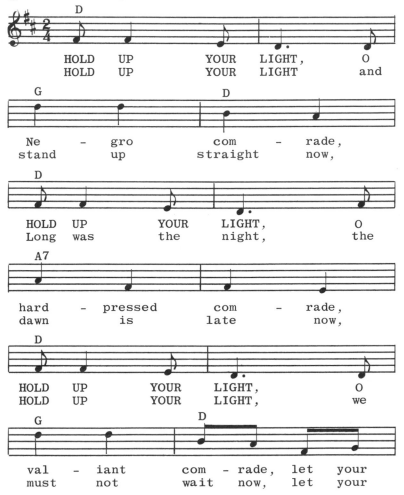

HOLD UP YOUR LIGHT, O
HOLD UP YOUR LIGHT and

Ne - gro com - rade,
stand up straight now,

HOLD UP YOUR LIGHT, O
Long was the night, the

hard - pressed com - rade, O
dawn is late now,

HOLD UP YOUR LIGHT, O
HOLD UP YOUR LIGHT, we

val - iant com - rade, let your
must not wait now, let your

Collected and arranged by Tom Glazer, © 1967, Songs Music, Inc., Scarborough, N.Y. All rights reserved.

147

A HOUSEWIFE'S LAMENT

A personal protest song found in the diary of Mrs. Sara A. Price of Ottawa, Illinois, some of whose sons were killed in the Civil War.

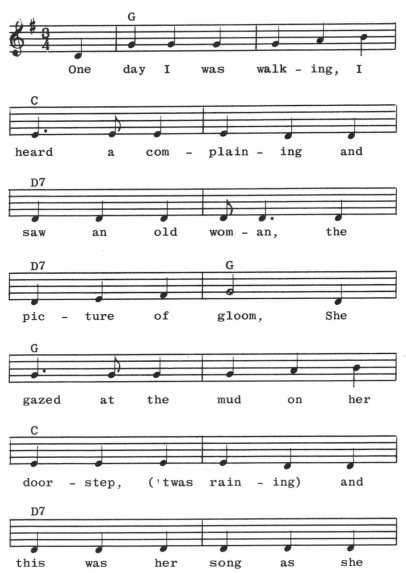

One day I was walk - ing, I heard a com - plain - ing and saw an old wom - an, the pic - ture of gloom, She gazed at the mud on her door - step, ('twas rain - ing) and this was her song as she

wish   it   to   be.

There's too much of worriment goes to a bonnet,
There's too much of ironing goes to a shirt,
There's nothing that pays for the
Time you waste on it,
There's nothing that lasts us but
Trouble and dirt.
In March it is mud, it is slush in December,
The midsummer breezes are loaded with dust.
In fall the leaves litter, in muddy September
The wallpaper rots and the candlesticks rust.

There are worms on the cherries and
Slugs on the roses,
And ants in the sugar and mice in the pies,
The rubbish of spiders no mortal supposes
And ravaging roaches and damaging flies.
It's sweeping at six and it's dusting at seven,
It's victuals at eight and it's dishes at nine.
It's potting and panning from ten to eleven
We scarce break our fast till we plan how to dine.

With grease and with grime from corner to center,
Forever at war and forever alert.
No rest for a day lest the enemy enter,
I spend my whole life in struggle with dirt.
Last night in my dreams I was stationed forever
On a far little rock in the midst of the sea.
My one chance of life was a ceaseless endeavor,
To sweep off the waves as they swept over me.

Alas! Twas no dream; ahead I behold it,
I see I am helpless my fate to avert.
She lay down her broom, her apron she folded,
She lay down and died and was buried in dirt.

Oh, life is a toil and love is a trouble,
And beauty will fade and riches will flee,
Pleasures, they dwindle and prices will double,
And nothing is as I would wish it to be.

HUELGA EN GENERAL (GENERAL STRIKE)

By LUIS VALDEZ

A song out of the four-year-old strike of 1965-1969 by grape-pickers around Delano, California. Most of the strikers are Spanish-speaking Mexican-Americans, some are Filipinos. They are led by Cesar Chavez, and after four years, talks between growers and workers were just beginning. Luis Valdez, who wrote this song, also started El Teatro Campesino (The Farm Workers Theater) in 1965 to bring the message of the struggles of the farm workers for union recognition to the rest of the country.

Has-ta Me- ji-co ha lle- ga-do la no-

ti - cia muy a - le - gre, que de

leerlo- es dif- fer- en - te, ____

Pues al pue-blo ya es-ta en con-tra los ran-

cher - os y en - grei- dos que a -

ca- ban con la - gen - te, ___

Y co- mo so-mos her- ma- nos la a -

leg - ria com - par - ti - mos con to -

dos los cam- pes - in - os. ___

Vi - va la re- vo- lu - cion, vi- va

nues - tra a- so - cia - cion, Vi - va

HUEL - GA EN GEN - ER - AL.

1.

2. F

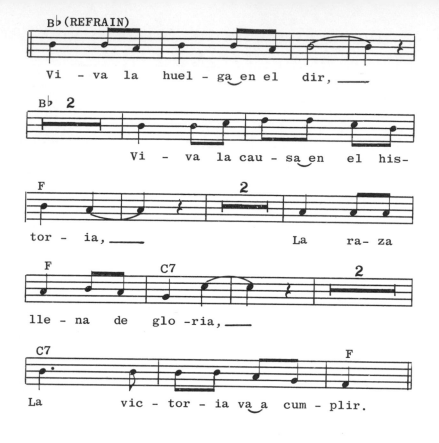

Bb (REFRAIN)

Vi - va la huel - ga en el dir, ____

Bb 2

Vi - va la cau - sa en el his-

F **2**

tor - ia, ____ La ra- za

F **C7** **2**

lle - na de glo -ria, ____

C7 **F**

La vic - tor - ia va a cum - plir.

TRANSLATION

Very happy news has reached Mexico,
Which sounds different if you read it,
Since the people are against it.
The ranchers and the haughty who mistreat them.
And since we're all brothers,
We'll share this happiness with all the farmers.
Long live the revolution.
Long live our association.
Long live the general strike.

Long live the strike in the "Dir". (division)
Long live our cause for history.
This race full of glory
A race full of glory will be fulfilled with victory.

154

THE HUSBAND WITH NO COURAGE IN HIM

To "protest" the lack of her husband's sexual sufficiency is the
lament of a wife, in this heartfelt effusion. It was collected in
the south of England.

Very Freely

As ___ I walked out one
sum -mer's day to view the fields and the
liz - ards spring - ing, I ___
saw two maid - ens stand -in' by, and ___
one of them her
hands was wring - in', and ___
all of her con - ver -

sa - tion___ was: "My hus-band's got no

cour - age in him, oh, dear, no,

oh, dear, no, My___ hus -band's got no

cour- age in him, oh, dear, no."

All sorts of meat I do preserve,
All sorts of drink that's fittin' for him,
Both oyster pies and rhubarb too,
But nothing will put courage in him.
    Oh dear no, oh dear no,
    Nothing will put courage in him,
    Oh dear no.

It's seven long years I've made his bed,
And six of them I've laid agin him,
And this morn I rose with my maidenhead,
Now that shows he's got no courage in him.
    Oh dear no, oh dear no.
    That shows he's got no courage in him,
    Oh dear no.

Come all pretty maids wherever you be,
Don't marry a man before you try him,
Lest you should sing a song like me,
Now, my husband's got no courage in him.
    Oh dear no, oh dear no,
    Me husband's got no courage in him,
    Oh dear no.

```
I wish to the Lord that he were dead,
And in his grave I'd quickly laid him;
Then I would try another one
That had a little courage in him.
    Oh dear yes, oh dear yes,
    That had a little courage in him,
    Oh dear yes.
```

I AM SOLD AND GOING TO GEORGIA

An interesting slave song, but apparently of white, not black, origin, from the WPA folksong collection in the Library of Congress.

SOLD AND GO- ING TO GEOR - GIA, Go___

sound the Ju - bi - lee.

I left my wife and child behind,
They'll never see my face again;
I am sold, and going to Georgia. . .

I am bound to yonder great rice swamp,
Where my poor bones will find a grave!
I am sold, and going to Georgia. . .

Farewell, my friends, I leave you all--
I am sold, but I have done no fault;
I am sold, and going to Georgia. . .

I DON'T WANNA BE LOST IN THE SLUMS

Eloquent alone is the title, and even more eloquent is this expression of an unknown writer in the Chicago Freedom Movement. It is based on the song "This Little Light of Mine."

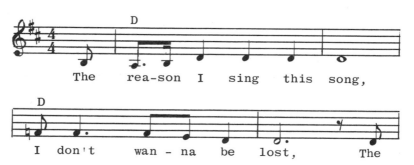

The rea-son I sing this song,

I don't wan - na be lost, The

From *Freedom Is a Constant Struggle*, comp. and ed. by Guy and Candie Carawan, © 1963, Oak Publications, a Div. of Embassy Music Corp., N.Y. Used by permission.

SLUMS. _____

The reason I live this life,
  I don't want to be lost,
The reason I live this life,
  I don't want to be lost,
The reason I live this life,
  I don't want to be lost,
I don't want to be lost in the slums.

The reason I sing this song,
  I don't want to be lost, etc.

The reason I join the movement, etc.

The reason I march downtown, etc.

The reason I go to jail, etc.

The reason I sacrifice, Lord, etc.

The reason I fight so hard, etc.

Days of the slums are numbered, etc.

Lost in the slums, Lord, etc.

The reason I live this life, etc.

I DON'T WANT TO BE A SOLDIER

Its origin is probably World War II, though some say it dates back to World War I. It's all the same to me, just as long as it doesn't date ahead to World War III. Probably of Cockney origin.

I DON'T WANT TO BE A SOL - DIER,
I don't want to go to war,
I would rath - er hang a - round
Pic - ca -dil - ly's un - der -ground and

Collected and arranged by Tom Glazer, © 1967, Songs Music, Inc., Scarborough, N.Y. All rights reserved.

live up - on the earn - ings of a

high - born la - dy,

I don't want a bul - let up me

arse-hole, nor want me bloom-in' knock-ers shot a-

way, I'd rath- er stay in Eng -land,

jol - ly, jol - ly Eng - a - land, and

for - ni - cate me bloom -in' life a -

way, Gor bli - mey,

I DON'T WANT YOUR MILLIONS, MISTER

By JIM GARLAND

Written by Jim Garland from an older, well-known song called "East Virginia." Garland was a brother of Aunt Molly Jackson, the source of several famous songs, and he wrote many songs about the struggles of miners in Kentucky in the 1930s. It was popularized in a recording in 1941 by the Almanac Singers.

I DON'T WANT _____ YOUR MIL-LIONS, MIS-TER, _____ I don't want _____ your dia-mond ring, _____ All I want _____ is the right to live, mis-ter, _____ Give me

back _____ my job a -

gain. _____

I don't want your Rolls-Royce, mister;
I don't want your pleasure yacht;
All I want is food for my babies;
Give to me my old job back.

We worked to build this country, mister,
While you enjoyed a life of ease;
You've stolen all that we built, mister;
Now our children starve and freeze.

Think me dumb if you wish, mister;
Call me green, or blue, or red;
This one thing I sure know, mister:
My hungry babies must be fed.

Take the two old parties, mister;
No difference in them I can see,
But with a Farmer-Labor party
We could set the people free.

IF YOU MISS ME FROM THE BACK OF THE BUS

Words by CARVER NEBLETT

An integration song sung by black and white students in various situations and circumstances. It started out at the Students Nonviolent Coordinating Committee (SNCC).

IF YOU MISS___ ME FROM THE

BACK OF THE BUS, ____

And you can't find __ me no - where,

Come on up _____ to the

front of the bus, ____

I'll be rid - in' up there,

I'll be rid - in' up there,

I'll be rid - in' up there,

Come on up ___ to the

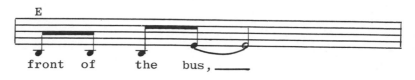

front of the bus, ___

I'll be rid - in' up there.

If you miss me from the front of the bus,
And you can't find me nowhere,
Come on up to the driver's seat,
I'll be drivin' up there.
I'll be drivin' up there,
I'll be drivin' up there,
Come on up to the front of the bus,
I'll be drivin' up there.

If you miss me from Jackson State,
And you can't find me nowhere,
Come on over to Ole Miss,
I'll be studyin' over there. . .

If you miss me from knockin' on doors,
And you can't find me nowhere,
Come on down to the registrar's room,
I'll be the registrar there. . .

If you miss me from the cotton field,
And you can't find me nowhere,
Come on down to the court house,
I'll be voting right there. . .

If you miss me from the picket line,
And you can't find me nowhere,
Come on down to the jail house,
I'll be rooming down there. . .

If you miss me from the Mississippi River,
And you can't find me nowhere,
Come on down to the city pool,
I'll be swimming in there. . .

I'M GOING TO JOIN THE ARMY

Still another moving complaint by a sweetheart about her lover going off to war—the Civil War, in this case. Again, his name is Johnny.

I'M GOING TO JOIN THE AR - MY, I'm going to vol - un - teer, ___ I'm going to be a sol - dier be - fore an - oth - er year.

I'm going to Pensacola
To tarry for a while,
Far from you, my darling,
More than a hundred mile.

O hear the cannons roaring,
O see the bullets fly;
O hear the drum a-beating
To drown the deadly cry.

O, stay at home, dear Johnny,
Make me your lawful wife;
If you go to Pensacola
They'll surely take your life.

They'll put you in the centre,
It's there you will be slain,
It'll burst my heart asunder
To never see you again.

Let me go with you, Johnny:
I'll travel by your side,
And when the war is over,
You can make me your bride.

No, stay at home, dear Nancy,
And live a single life,
And if I do come back again,
I'll make you my wife.

They marched him through the country,
They marched him through the town;
He marched to Pensacola
And there they shot him down.

I'm weary of the fighting,
I'm weary of the wars;
Farewell to you, my darling,
I'll never see you no more.

I'M GONNA SIT AT THE WELCOME TABLE

Adapted from the old spiritual.

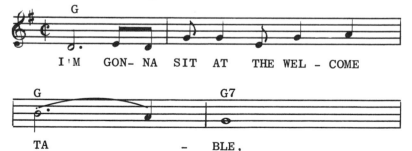

I'M GON- NA SIT AT THE WEL - COME

TA   - BLE,

I'M ON MY WAY

A recent adaptation of an old song, possibly of Underground Railroad origin, possibly of Gospel origin.

I'M ON MY WAY _____ to Ca-naan land, _____ I'M ON MY WAY_____ to Ca - naan land, _____ I'M ON MY___ WAY_____ to Ca - naan land, _____ I'M ON MY WAY, _____ Great God, I'M ON MY WAY. _____

I asked my brother to come with me,   3x
I'M ON MY WAY, great God, I'M ON MY WAY.

I asked my sister to come with me,   3x - etc.

I asked my boss to let me go,   3x - etc.

If he says no, I'll go anyhow,   3x - etc.

If you won't go, let your children go,   3x - etc.

If you won't go, let your mother go,   3x - etc.

I'M ON MY WAY and I won't turn back,   3x - etc.

IN SOLITARY

A song of unusual interest hitherto unpublished in the West. Along with a few others of the same type, it was smuggled out of Soviet labor camps by escapees in the late 1940s during Stalin's regime. The Russian words are transliterated for the sake of pronunciation. (A recent conservative estimate indicates that at least 20 million people perished during Stalin's purges, a figure almost impossible to comprehend.)

AKH   VOT   SEE -ZHOO   YA   VO__   DEE - NO -

CHKEH_____   VOK - NO   TYOO -

Collected and arranged by Tom Glazer, © 1967, Songs Music, Inc., Scarborough, N.Y. All rights reserved.

REM - NO - YEH GLA - ZHOO_____

_____ AH SLO - ZI KA - TYAT - SI TAK

VOT___ ROO -CHYA - MEE PO

EES - KHOO - DA - LO ____ MOO LEE-

TSOO. _____

MENYA AKLEEKNOOT CHASOVIYE
AKLEEKNOOT RAZ AKLEEKNOOT DVA
ANEE VZVEDOOT KOORKEE STALNIYE
NAVEK OOBYOOT MENYA.

GDYE PAKHARONYAT YA NE ZNAYOO
EE NYE OOZNAYOO NEEKAGDA
ZA SHTO ZA SHTO TEEPER YA BRATSI PRABADAYOO
TAKEEYE YOONIYE GADA.

Translation

Here I am, sitting IN SOLITARY,
Looking out the jail window
And tears roll in streams
From my emaciated face.

The Guards will summon me,
Summon me once, summon me twice,
They will cock their rifles
And will kill me forever.

Where I'll be buried, I don't know
And I'll never find out,
Why should I perish so young?
Why should I perish so young?

IT ISN'T NICE

By MALVINA REYNOLDS

A very interesting song by Malvina Reynolds, who has written many good songs, notably "Little Boxes" (see index). Fighting for one's rights in many senses is really not very "nice."

IT IS-N'T NICE to block the
door-way, IT IS-N'T NICE to go to
jail, There are nic-er ways to
do it, but the nice ways al-ways

fail, IT IS - N'T NICE, IT IS - N'T NICE, you told us once, you told us twice, But if that is Free -dom's price, we don't mind. _____

It isn't nice to carry banners,
Or to sit in on the floor,
Or to shout our cry of Freedom
At the hotel or the store,
It isn't nice, it isn't nice,
You told us once, you told us twice,
But if that is Freedom's price, we don't mind.

We have tried negotiations
And the three-man picket line,
Mr. Charlie didn't see us
And he might as well be blind,
Now our new ways aren't nice
When we deal with men of ice,
But if that is Freedom's price, we don't mind.

How about those years of lynchings,
And the shot in Evers' back?
Did you say it wasn't proper?
Did you stand out on the track?
You were quiet, just like mice,
Now you say we aren't nice,
But if that is Freedom's price, we don't mind.

It isn't nice to block the doorway,
It isn't nice to go to jail,
There are nicer ways to do it,
But the nice ways always fail,
It isn't nice, it isn't nice,
But thanks for your advice,
'Cause if that is Freedom's price, we don't mind.

IT'S A BRAVE NEW WORLD

Words by TOM GLAZER

I wrote this in 1967 for the Preserve the Hudson River Committee, conservationist group. A conservationist has declared recently that he has almost given up on the conservation struggle because the American people "just don't give a damn" and because of the population explosion.

It's fun to wake in sum -mer to the
sing - ing of the choirs of the
rob - ins and the black -birds which are
nest - ing in the wires, Which are

better far to nest in as the

nasty tree expires, IT'S A

BRAVE, BRAVE, BRAVE NEW WORLD.

Glory, glory, Henry Hudson,

soon your waters will be mud, son,

let's replace your trees ___ with ___

electricities, IT'S A

BRAVE, BRAVE, BRAVE NEW WORLD.

It's a drag to sail your sailboat which you
Once thought quite a treat,
Sailing is so corny when you
Suffer from the heat,
Just listen to the generator's
Rich, refreshing beat,
In a brave, brave, brave new world.

There used to be corn in Cornwall and there
Used to be a wall,
And the sweethearts used to walk along
The river in the Fall,
Now they hear about Nature from Tex Antoine,
They don't need Nature at all,
IT'S A BRAVE, BRAVE, BRAVE NEW WORLD.

Katherine Cornell, and Helen Hayes,
Mitch Miller and others too,
They live along the Hudson just as
Thousands of people do,
Because they want to change the river
To a factory view
In a brave, brave, brave new world.

IT'S ME, O LORD

A Depression version of a spiritual of the same title: "It's Me,
O Lord, Standing in the Need of Prayer."

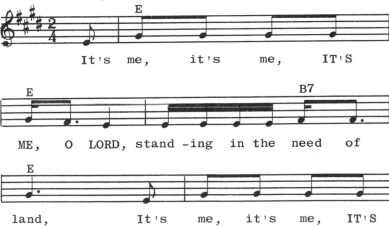

It's me, it's me, IT'S
ME, O LORD, stand -ing in the need of
land, It's me, it's me, IT'S

From *Hard Hitting Songs for Hard Hit People*, by A. Lomax, W.
Guthrie, P. Seeger, © 1947, Oak Publications, a Div. of Embassy
Music Corp., N.Y. Used by permission.

ME, O LORD, stand-ing in the need of

land, 'Tain't the

bank - er, 'tain't the plant - er, but IT'S

ME, O LORD, stand-ing in the need of

land, 'Tain't the

bank - er, 'tain't the plant - er, but IT'S

ME, O LORD, stand-ing in the need of land.

It's me, it's me, it's me, O Lord,
Standing in the need of a home.
It's me, it's me, it's me, O Lord,
Standing in the need of a home.
Taint the lawyer, taint the merchant
But it's me, O Lord,
Standing in the need of a home.

```
Taint the lawyer, taint the merchant,
But it's me, O Lord,
Standing in the need of a home.

It's me, it's me, it's me, O Lord,
Standing in the need of bread.
It's me, it's me, it's me, O Lord,
Standing in the need of bread.
Taint the gorcer, taint the baker,
But it's me, O Lord,
Standing in the need of bread.
Taint the grocer, taint the baker,
But it's me, O Lord,
Standing in the need of bread.
```

JEFFERSON AND LIBERTY

Sung during the election campaign of 1800 when Thomas Jefferson was running for President. One of his chief campaign pledges was the repeal of the Alien and Sedition Laws, which empowered a President to suppress (undemocratically) political opposition and to expel aliens, and which contained other oppressive measures. Feelings ran high. The song had been sung earlier in England under the title "Wilkes and Liberty" and later during Lincoln's campaign under the title "Lincoln and Liberty."

Vigorously

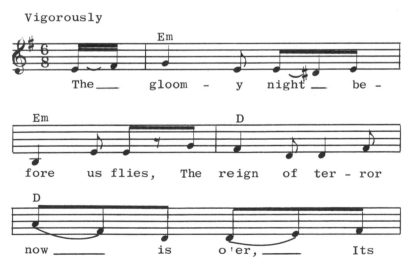

gags in-qui - si -tors and spies, Its

herds__ of har -pies are no more.

Re - joice, Co - lum - bia's

sons, re -joice, To ty - rants nev - er

bend__ the knee, but join with heart and

soul _____ and voice For

JEF - FER -SON__ AND LI - BER - TY.

No lordling here, with gorging jaws
Shall wring from industry the food;
Nor fiery bigot's holy laws
Lay waste our fields and streets in blood!

Here strangers from a thousand shores
Compelled by tyranny to roam,
Shall find, amidst abundant stores,
A nobler and happier home.

Here Art shall lift her laurelled head,
Wealth, Industry, and Peace, divine;
And where dark, pathless forests spread,
Rich fields and lofty cities shine.

From Europe's wants and woes remote,
A friendly waste of waves between,
Here plenty cheers the humblest cot,
And smiles on every village green.

Here free as air, expanded space,
To every soul and sect shall be --
That sacred privilege of our race --
The worship of the Deity.

Let foes to freedom dread the name;
But should they touch the sacred tree,
Twice fifty thousand swords would flame
For Jefferson and liberty.

From Georgia to Lake Champlain,
From seas to Mississippi's shore,
Ye sons of freedom loud proclaim --
"The reign of terror is no more."

JOE HILL

By EARL ROBINSON and ALFRED HAYES

The very famous paean to our first talented writer of protest songs, whose real name was Joseph Hillstrom. Have you ever heard about the patient who walks into his psychoanalyst's office, lies down on the couch, and says, "Doc, I dreamed I saw Joe Hill last night"?

I dreamed I saw JOE
"In Salt Lake, Joe, by

HILL last night, a - live as you and
God, "says I, Him stand -ing by my

me, Says I, "But Joe, you're
bed, "They framed you on a

ten years dead." "I nev - er died," says
mur - der charge,"Says Joe, "But I ain't

he, "I nev - er died," says he.
dead," Says Joe, "But I ain't dead."

"The copper bosses killed you, Joe,
They shot you, Joe," says I.
"Takes more than guns to kill a man,"
Says Joe, "I didn't die."
Says Joe, "I didn't die."

And standing there as big as life,
And smiling with his eyes,
Joe says, "What they forgot to kill
Went on to organize."
Went on to organize."

"Joe Hill ain't dead," he says to me.
"Joe Hill ain't never died.
Where workingmen are out on strike,
Joe Hill is at their side."
Joe Hill is at their side."

"From San Diego up to Maine,
In every mine and mill
Where workers strike and organize,"
Says he, "You'll find Joe Hill."
Says he, "You'll find Joe Hill."

I dreamed I saw Joe Hill last night,
Alive as you and me.
Says I, "But Joe, you're ten years dead."
"I never died," says he.
"I never died," says he.

JOHNNY, I HARDLY KNEW YOU

An eighteenth-century Irish song, written about an Irish soldier
who returns maimed from the English wars. The tune was
later used in this country for the much more romantic soldier
song "When Johnny Comes Marching Home," and still later
for "Ghost Riders in the Sky."

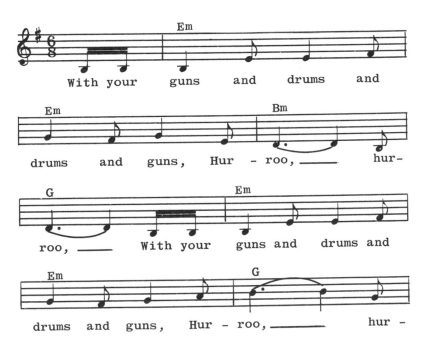

roo,_____ With your guns and drums and
drums and guns, the en-e-my near-ly
slew you, oh, my dar-lin' dear, you
look so queer, Oh JOHN-NY, I HARD-LY
KNEW YOU. _____

Where are your legs that used to run?
Hurroo, hurroo,
Where are the legs that used to run?
Hurroo, hurroo,
Where are the legs that used to run
When first you went to carry a gun?
I fear your dancing days are done,
JOHNNY, I HARDLY KNEW YOU.

You haven't an arm and you haven't a leg,
Hurroo, hurroo,
You haven't an arm and you haven't a leg,
Hurroo, hurroo,
You haven't an arm and you haven't a leg,
You're an eyeless, boneless, chickenless egg,
You'll have to be put with a bone to beg,
JOHNNY, I HARDLY KNEW YOU.

They're rolling out the drums again,
Hurroo, hurroo,
They're rolling out the drums again,
Hurroo, hurroo,
They're rolling out the drums again,
But they'll never take our sons again,
No, they'll never take our sons again,
Johnny, I'm swearing to you.

Where are your legs that used to run?
Hurroo, hurroo,
Where are the legs that used to run?
Hurroo, hurroo,
Where are the legs that used to run
When first you went to carry a gun?
I fear your dancing days are done,
JOHNNY, I HARDLY KNEW YOU.

JOHNNY, WON'T YOU RAMBLE

From the Archives of American Folksong at the Library of
Congress. Look at the words and think what slavery means.
And oppression. And depression.

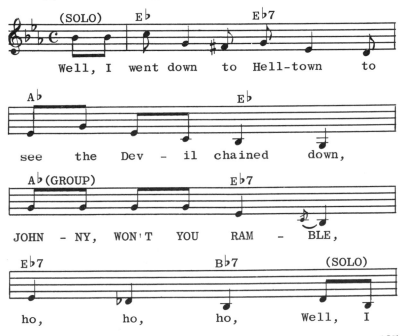

Well, I went down to Hell-town to
see the Dev-il chained down,
JOHN-NY, WON'T YOU RAM-BLE,
ho, ho, ho, Well, I

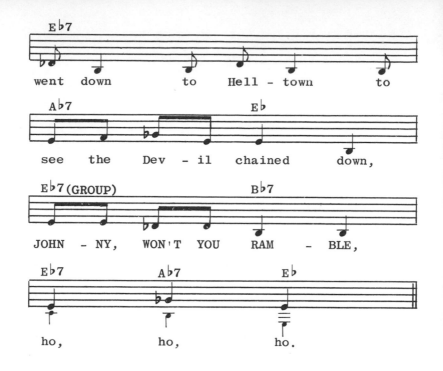

went down to Hell - town to see the Dev - il chained down,
JOHN - NY, WON'T YOU RAM - BLE, ho, ho, ho.

I looked up on the hill
And spied old Master ridin',
Johnny, won't you ramble, ho, ho, ho,
Had a bull whip in one hand,
Cowhide in the other,
Johnny, won't you ramble, ho, ho, ho.

Pocket full of leather strings
To tie your hands together,
Johnny, won't you ramble, ho, ho, ho,
Oh Master, don't whup me,
I'll give you half a dollar,
Johnny, won't you ramble, ho, ho, ho.

Oh no, Bully Boy,
I'd rather hear you holler,
Johnny, won't you ramble, ho, ho, ho,
Oh Master, don't you whup me,
I'll give you half a dollar,
Johnny, won't you ramble, ho, ho, ho.

KEEP ON PUSHING

A fine effort out of the Chicago Freedom Movement, recorded by the Impressions.

KEEP ON _____ PUSH- ING,

KEEP ON PUSH- ING.

I've got to KEEP ON _____ PUSH -ING,

mmm, _____ I can't __ stop

now, Move up

a lit -tle high - er,

some - way, __ some - how,

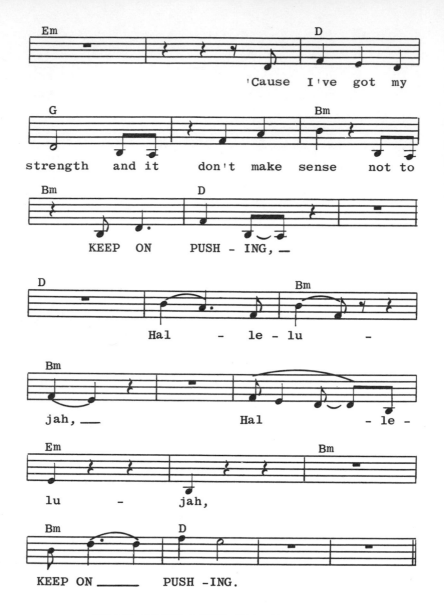

KEEP YOUR EYES ON THE PRIZE

A freedom song version of the great spiritual "Mary Had a Golden Chain," also called "Hold On."

Paul and Silas begin to shout
The jail door opened and they
    walked on out
Keep your eyes on the prize, hold on.

Freedom's name is mighty sweet,
Soon one day we're gonna meet.
Keep your eyes on the prize, hold on.

Got my hand on the Gospel plow,
I wouldn't take nothing for my
    journey now.
Keep your eyes on the prize, hold on.

The only chain that a man can stand,
Is that chain of hand in hand.
Keep your eyes on the prize, hold on.

The only thing we did wrong,
Stayed in the wilderness a day too
    long,
Keep your eyes on the prize, hold on.

But the one thing we did right,
Was the day we started to fight.
Keep your eyes on the prize, hold on.

We're gonna board that big Greyhound,
Carryin' love from town to town.
Keep your eyes on the prize, hold on.

We're gonna ride for civil rights,
We're gonna ride both black and white.
Keep your eyes on the prize, hold on.

We've met jail and violence too,
But God's love has seen us through.
Keep your eyes on the prize, hold on.

Haven't been to heaven but I've been told,
Streets up there are paved with gold.
Keep your eyes on the prize, hold on.

KEVIN BARRY

Another very popular big-city folksong of the 1930s, and still often sung even though its origin is purely Irish. Kevin Barry was hung by the British in a Dublin jail in 1920 during the Irish-English struggles of that period. A long time ago, I noticed a rather startling coincidence, if it is that: the time value of the notes in "Kevin Barry" are exactly the same as those of the famous Russian folksong "Stenka Razin," although the melodies are different.

Early on a Monday morning, high up-
lad of eighteen summers, yet there's

on the gallows tree, KEV - IN
no one can deny As he

BAR - RY gave his young life for the
went to death that morn - ing, proud-ly

1. cause of li - ber - ty. Just a

2. held his head on high.

"Shoot me like an Irish soldier;
Do not hang me like a dog;
For I fought for Ireland's freedom
On that cold September morn --

All around that little bakery
Where we fought them hand to hand.
Shoot me like an Irish soldier
For I fought to free Ireland."

Another martyr for old Ireland,
Another murder for the crown!
Brutal laws to crush the Irish
Could not keep their spirit down.
Lads like Barry are no cowards:
From their foes they do not fly,
For their bravery always has been
Ireland's cause to live or die.

Just before he faced the hangman
In his lonely prison cell,
British soldiers tortured Barry
Just because he would not tell
All the names of his companions,
Other things they wished to know;
"Turn informer and we'll free you."
Proudly Barry answered, "No."

THE KLAN

By DAVID ARKIN and ALAN GREY

Alan Grey, one writer of this song, is known to millions of movie-goers as Alan Arkin.

The coun - try - side was
cold and still, __ There was a cross up -

on the hill,— This cold cross wore a
burn-ing hood — To hide its rot - ten
heart of wood, —————
Fa - ther, — I hear the
i - ron sound of hoof -beats on the
fro — zen ground. —————

Down from the hills the riders came,
Jesus, it was a crying shame,
To see the blood upon their whips,
And hear the snarling of their lips.
Mother, I feel a stabbing pain,
Blood flows down like a summer rain.

Now each one wore a mask of white,
To hide his cruel face from sight,
And each one sucked a little breath
Out of the empty lungs of death.
Sister, lift my bloody head,
It's so lonesome to be dead.

He who travels with THE KLAN
Is a monster, not a man.
Underneath that white disguise
I have looked into his eyes.
Brother, will you stand with me?
It's not easy to be free.

KUM-BA-YA

Additional words and new music by LEE HAYS,
FRED HELLERMAN, RONNIE GILBERT, and
ERIK DARLING

Originally an American Negro spiritual called "Come By Here, Lord" (see index), this song has had a very unusual journey. It was taken by missionaries to Africa where it underwent a sea-change in the manner of transmitted folksongs. Now it has returned to this country with further changes.

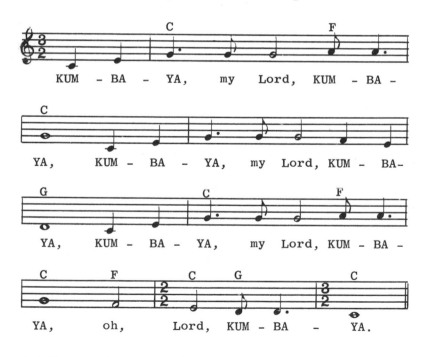

KUM - BA - YA, my Lord, KUM - BA -
YA, KUM - BA - YA, my Lord, KUM - BA-
YA, KUM - BA - YA, my Lord, KUM - BA -
YA, oh, Lord, KUM - BA - YA.

Someone's weeping, Lord, KUM-BA-YA,
Someone's weeping, Lord, KUM-BA-YA,
Someone's weeping, Lord, KUM-BA-YA,
Oh, Lord, KUM-BA-YA.

Someone's singing, Lord, KUM-BA-YA,
    etc.

Someone's praying, Lord, KUM-BA-YA,
    etc.

The world's in danger, Lord, KUM-BA-YA,
    etc.

Tell the leaders, Lord, KUM-BA-YA,
    etc.

We must act now, Lord, KUM-BA-YA,
    etc.

Sing out loud and clear, KUM-BA-YA,
etc.

LABOR'S ENDLESS CHAIN

An obscure three-note song whose directions alone make it worthy of disinterring: "With relentless regularity." "Repeat endlessly."

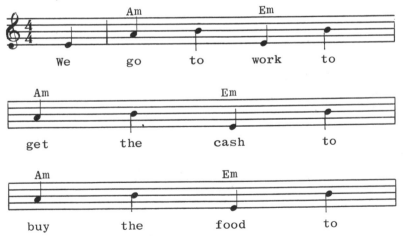

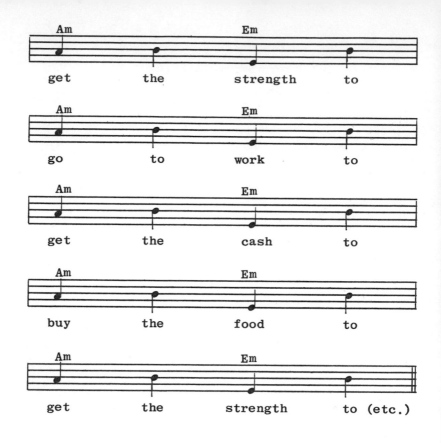

LA MUJER DE PANCHO FRANCO

Collected in Madrid in 1961 from a student. The melody is one of the most famous ones from the Spanish Civil War, known as "El Ejercito del Ebro, Ay Carmela" or "Viva La Quinze Brigada." From a collection of anti-fascist songs published in Italy and France in 1962 and 1963.

From *Chansons de la nouvelle résistance espagnole*, Paris, 1963, © 1962, Enaudi Editore, Torino. Used by permission.

LA MU - JER DE PAN-CHO FRAN-CO, rum- ba la

rum- ba, la rum-bum ba. LA MU -

ba. No co - ci - na con car -

bon, __ Ay Ma - nue - la! Ay, Ma -

nue - la! __ No co - ci - na con car -

bon, __ Ay Ma - nue - la! Ay Ma -

nue - la! _____

Pero cocina con cuernos,
rumba, la rumba, la rumbumba
Pero cocina con cuernos,
rumba, la rumba, la rumbumba

de su marido el cabrón,
Ay Manuela, Ay Manuela,
de su marido el cabrón,
Ay Manuela, Ay Manuela.

197

> The wife of Pancho Franco,
> Rumba, rumba, la rumbaba (twice)
> Doesn't use any firewood
> Ay Manuela, Ay Manuela.(twice)
>
> She cooks with horns
> Rumba, rumba, la rumbaba (twice)
> With her horned husband*
> Ay Manuela, ay Manuela. (twice)

> * To be "horned" is to be cuckolded,
>   A concept going back to Roman times
>   And a common expression in Romance
>   Languages.

LAST NIGHT I HAD THE STRANGEST DREAM

By ED McCURDY

This song couldn't possibly be simpler in its melody and in its lyric. It has been recorded often and is spreading its peace message around the world.

Moderately

LAST   NIGHT   I   HAD   THE
(And)   when   the   pa -   per

STRAN- GEST___ DREAM, I'd ___ nev - er
was   all___ signed, And a   mil - lion

dreamed ___   be - fore, _____ I
cop   -   ies made, _____ They

dreamed / all   the / joined   world / hands   had / and

all   a   - greed   to   put   an
bowed their heads And grate - ful

end   to   war.   I
pray - ers were prayed.   And the

dreamed   I   saw   a
peo - ple   in   the

might - y   room And the room was
streets be - low were danc - ing

full   of   men,   And the
'round and 'round,   While

pa - per   they   were
swords and guns and

sign - ing said They'd nev - er
u - ni - forms Were scat - tered

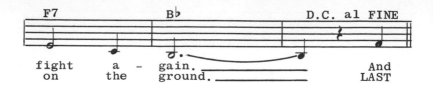

fight a - gain. And
on the ground. LAST

LE CHANT DES PARTISANS

A powerful song of the French Resistance of World War II.

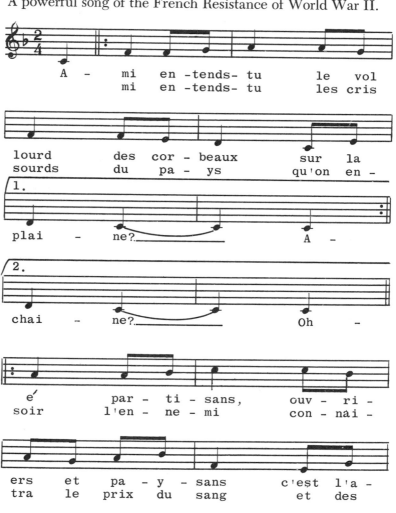

A - mi en -tends- tu le vol
mi en -tends- tu les cris

lourd des cor - beaux sur la
sourds du pa - ys qu'on en -

1.
plai - ne?_____ A -

2.
chai - ne?_____ Oh -

e' par - ti - sans, ouv - ri -
soir l'en - ne - mi con - nai -

ers et pa - y - sans c'est l'a -
tra le prix du sang et des

lar - me! Ce lar - mes!

Montez de la mine,
Descendez des collines camarades!
Sortez de la paille les fusils,
La mitraille les grenades!
Ohé les tueurs, a la balle
Ou au couteau, tuez vite!
Ohé saboteur, attention
A ton fardeau Dynamite!

C'est nous qui brisons les barreaux
Des prisons pour nos frères
La haine à nos trousses et la faim
Qui nous pousse la misère
Il est des pays ou les gens au creux
Des lits font des rêves
Ici, nous, vois-tu, nous on marche,
Nous l'on tue, nous l'on crève!

Ici chacun sait ce qu'il veut,
Ce qu'il fait quand il passe
Ami, si tu tombes, un ami sort de
L'ombre prend ta place
Demain du sang noir sechera au
Grand soleil sur la route
Sifflez, compagnons ,dans la nuit
La liberté nous écoute!

TRANSLATION

Oh friend, can you hear, hear the
Flight overhead of the raven?
Oh friend, can you hear, hear the
Faint muffled cry of our country?
Arise, partisans, rise, you tillers
Of the land, rise, you workers,
The hangmen shall pay for the
Bloodshed and the tears and the sorrow!

Come down from the hills and come
Out of the mines, oh, my comrades,
Dig up from the earth hidden
Rifles, grenades and machine-guns,
Tonight you shall kill, use your guns
And use your knives, kill them swiftly!
Take care, saboteur, for it's
Precious dynamite that you carry.

It's we who are breaking the
Bonds that imprison our brothers,
Though hunger may haunt us, our
Hate is the food that sustains us,
Oh, many the lands where the people
In their slumber lie dreaming,
But here, here we march, here we
Fight and kill and die for our freedom!

For each of us knows what he wants,
What he does as he passes,
My friend, if you fall, then a friend
Takes your place from the shadows,
At sunrise, the blood of the raven
Will be dry on the highway!
Oh, sing, comrades, sing, through the
Night, oh comrades, sing, freedom listen!

LITTLE BOXES

By MALVINA REYNOLDS

A very happy idea about a potentially very sad hang-up. It is
Malvina Reynolds' happiest hit.

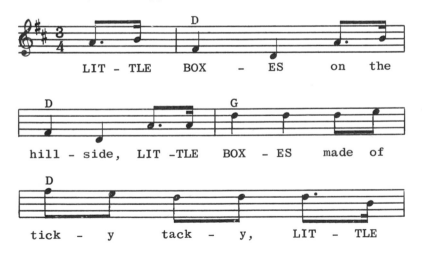

LIT - TLE   BOX – ES   on the
hill - side, LIT -TLE   BOX - ES   made of
tick - y   tack - y,   LIT - TLE

All the people in the houses
All went to the university,
Where they were put in boxes
And they all came out the same.
And there's doctors and there's lawyers
And business executives,
And they're all made out of ticky tacky
And they all look just the same.

And they all play on the golf course
And drink their martinis dry,
And they all have pretty children
And the children go to school,
And the children go to summer camp
And then to the university,
Where they are put in boxes
And they come out all the same.

And the boys go into business
And marry and raise a family,
In boxes made of ticky tacky
And they all look just the same.
There's a green one and a pink one
And a blue one and a yellow one,
And they're all made out of ticky tacky
And they all look just the same.

LONESOME TRAVELER

By LEE HAYS

This song is neither a peace song, nor a freedom song, nor a protest song directly, but perhaps it is all of these indirectly. We are all lonesome travelers although it is dubious that "one of these days I'm gonna stop all my traveling."

LONE - SOME TRAV- EL - ER,

I am a lone - ly and a

LONE - SOME TRAV - EL - ER,

I've been a - trav - el - in'

on.

I traveled here and then I traveled yonder, well
I traveled here and then I traveled yonder, well
I traveled here and then I traveled yonder, well
I been a-travelin' on.

I traveled cold and then I traveled hungry, well.

Traveled in the mountain, traveled down
    in the valley,

Traveled with the rich, traveled with the poor. .

One of these days I'm gonna stop all my travelin'.

Gonna keep on a-travelin' on the road to freedom
Gonna keep on a-travelin' on the road to freedom
Gonna keep on a-travelin' on the road to freedom
Gonna keep right on a-travelin' home.

LOS CUATRO GENERALES
(THE FOUR INSURGENT GENERALS)

Of all the songs that came over here from the Spanish Civil War, this was the first and probably the most popular. It is still very often requested at concerts and parties by innumerable people who are neither insurgents nor generals, which may indicate the triumph of music over politics.

LOS CUA - TRO GEN - ER - AL - ES,_____ LOS CUA - TRO GEN - ER - AL - ES,_____ LOS CUA - TRO GEN - ER - AL - ES, ma - mi - ta mi - a, Que se han al - za - do, Que se han al - za- do._____

LYNDON JOHNSON TOLD THE NATION

By TOM PAXTON

A protest song about what came to be known in the middle 1960s as the "credibility gap."

I got a let-ter from L. B. J. that said, "This is your luck-y day, It's time to put your khak-i trous-ers on. We've got a job for you to do, Dean Rusk has caught the A-sian flu and we are send-ing you to Vi-et-nam."

And LYN- DON JOHN- SON TOLD THE NA - TION,

"Have no fear of es - ca - la - tion,

I am try- ing ev - 'ry-one to please.

Tho' it is - n't real - ly war, we're

send - ing fif - ty thou - sand more to

help save Vi - et-nam from Vi-et-nam -ese.

They sent me to some swampy hole,
We went out on a night patrol,
Just who was who was very hard to tell,
With Martha Ray and thirteen mayors,
Half of Congress, six ball players and
Ronald Reagan yelling, "Give 'em hell!"

It didn't take us very long
To run into the Viet Cong,
We had our loyal allies to count on,
And as the bullets danced around,
I thought I heard the thundering sound
Of loyal allies half way to Saigon.

The word came from the very top
That soon the shooting war would stop,
The pockets of resistance were so thin,
There just remained some troubled spots,
Like Vietnam, Detroit and Watts
And Bobby Kennedy and Ho Chi Minh.

So here I sit in this big rice paddy
Wondering about Big Daddy,
And I know that Lyndon loves me so.
I'm one of the chosen men,
But somehow I remember when
He told me that I'd never have to go.

THE MAN THAT WATERS THE WORKERS' BEER

Words by PADDY RYAN

Of English origin with an Irish tune, "The Son of a Gambolier,"
the melody was also used in the famous American song, "Rambling Wreck From Georgia Tech."

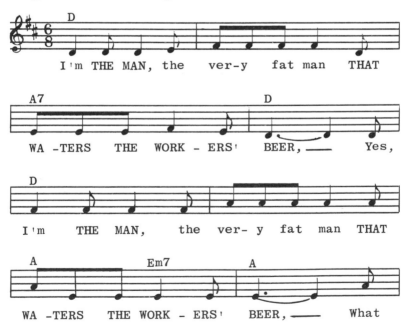

I'm THE MAN, the ver-y fat man THAT

WA -TERS THE WORK - ERS' BEER, —— Yes,

I'm THE MAN, the ver- y fat man THAT

WA -TERS THE WORK - ERS' BEER, —— What

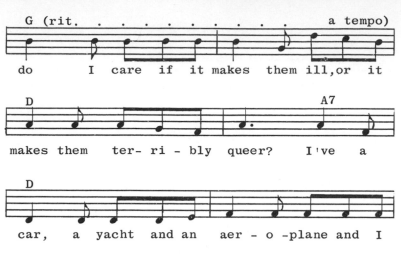

do   I care if it makes them ill, or it

makes them   ter- ri - bly queer?   I've   a

car,   a   yacht and an   aer - o -plane and I

wa - ters   the   work - ers'   beer. Now,

When I makes the workers' beer
I puts in strychinine,
Some methylated spirits
And a drop of paraffin.
But since a brew so terribly strong
Might make them terribly queer,
I reaches my hand for the water tap
And I waters the workers' beer.

A drop of good beer is good for a man
Who's thirsty, tired and hot
And sometimes I has a drop for myself
From a very special lot;
But a fat and healthy working class
Is the thing that I most fear,
So I reaches my hand for the water tap
And I waters the workers' beer.

Now ladies fair, beyond compare,
Be ye maid or wife,
Oh, sometimes lend a thought for one
Who leads a wand'ring life.
The water rates are shockingly high
And chemicals are so dear,
So there isn't the profit there used to be
When I water the workers' beer.

MANY THOUSANDS GONE

Yet another adaptation of a great spiritual. John Cheever calls religion "the ultimate ecstasy"; it is not difficult to see how this intense feeling is transformed into feelings of and for peace and freedom.

No more keep-ing quiet for me,
no more, no more,
No more keep-ing quiet for me,
MAN - Y THOU - SANDS GONE.

No more nuclear tests for me,
No more, no more
No more nuclear tests for me,
MANY THOUSANDS GONE.

No more fallout deaths for me,
      etc.

No more mushroom clouds for me,
      etc.

No more standing still for me,
      etc.

MANYURA, MANYAH

By MATT McGINN

There are all kinds of protest. This one may be the only one of its kind in song. It is Scottish, of course. English equivalents of some dialect words therein: wi', with; dain, doing; hawking, mining; toon, town; aroon, around; broon, brown.

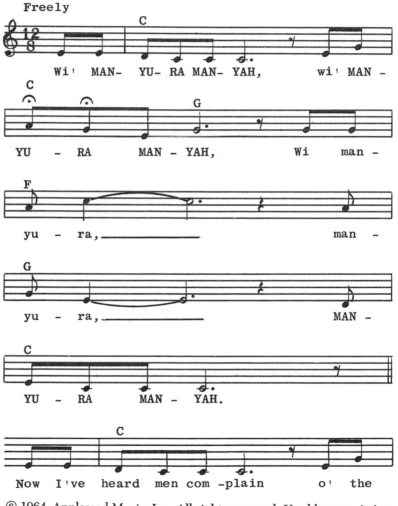

jobs that they're dain when they're hawk - ing _____ the coal or___ dig - ging the drain, But what - ev - er they are, there is none that com - pare with a man that sets shov-'ling MAN-YU- RA MAN- YAH.

The streets o' the toon
Were all covered aroon'
With stuff that was colorful, golden,
    and broon.
It was put there, of course,
By a big Clydesdale horse,
And they called it manyura, manyura,
    manyah.

I followed its track
Wi' a shovel and sack
And as often as no'
Wi' a pain in my back.
It was all for the rent
And the beautiful scent
Of manyura, manyura, manyura,
    manyah.

But I'm feeling gae sore
For my job's been ta'en o'er
And everything new
Is mechanical power;
And there's nothing for me
But the sweet memory
Of manyura, manyura, manyura,
    manyah.

MARY'S LITTLE LOT

This was collected during the WPA Writers Project days around 1940 and inveighs against minority ownership of the land.

Mar - y had a lit - tle lot, a
lit - tle lot, a lit - tle lot,
Mar - y had a lit - tle lot, the
soil was ver - y poor. But

still she kept it all the same,

all the same, all the same, but

still she kept it all the same and

strug - gled to get more.
She kept the lot until one day
The people settled down -
And where a wilderness had been
Grew up a thriving town.

They grew, as population comes,
And Mary raised the rent.
With common food and raiment now,
She could not be content.

"What makes the lot keep Mary so?"
The starving people cry -
"Why, Mary keeps the lot, you know,"
The wealthy would reply.

Then Mary rented out her lot -
(She would not sell, you know) -
And waited patiently about
For prices still to grow.

She built her up a mansion fine -
Had bric-a-brac galore -
And every time the prices rose,
She raised the rent some more.

And so each one of you might be -
"Wealthy, refined and wise" -
If you had only hogged some land
And held it for the rise.

215

THE MERRY MINUET

By SHELDON HARNICK

Sheldon Harnick, who wrote this charming ditty, is better known for his music in *Fiddler on the Roof*. It was once recorded by the Kingston Trio.

They're ri-o-ting in Af-ri-ca, (whistle--------------------)They're star-ving in Spain, (whistle------------ ---) There's hur-ri-canes in Flor-i-da, (whistle--------------------) And Tex-as needs rain. (whistle----------------) The whole world is fes-ter-ing with un-hap-py souls, the French hate the Ger-mans, the

more. (whistle-------------------) But

we can be tran -quil and thank- ful and

proud, For man's been en - dowed with a

mush-room shaped cloud, And we know for

cer-tain that some love- ly day,

Some - one will set the spark off and

we will all be blown a - way. They're

ri - o - ting in Af - ri - ca,

(whistle--------------------)There's strife in I -

ran, (whistle---------------) What

na -ture does - n't do to us,

(whistle----------------)will be done by our fel-low

man. (whistle------------------)

THE MIDNIGHT SPECIAL

The legend is that if the train comes by at midnight and the light shines in your cell, you may go free, according to Huddie Ledbetter, better known as Leadbelly.

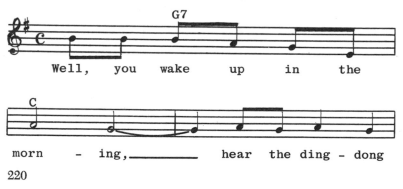

Well, you wake up in the

morn - ing,_____ hear the ding - dong

220

Let the MID - NIGHT SPE - CIAL ___ ___ shine its ev-er lov-in' light on you.

If you ever go to Houston, you better walk right,
You better not stagger and you better not fight,
Or Sheriff Benson will arrest you,
He will carry you down,
If de jury finds you guilty,
You'll be penitentiary bound.

Yonder come Miss Rosie,
How in the worl' do you know?
I can tell by her apron and de dress she wo',
Umbrella on her shoulder,
Piece o' paper in her hand,
Well, I heard her tell the Captain,
"I want my man."

I'm gwine away an' leave you,
An' my time ain't long,
De man is gonna call me an' I'm goin' home,
Then I'll be done all my grievin',
Whoopin', hollin' and a-cryin',
Then I'll be done all my studyin'
'Bout my great long time.

Well, de biscuits on de table
Just as hard as any rock,
If you try to swallow dem,
Break a convict's heart,
My sister wrote a letter,
My mother wrote a card:
"If you want to come and see us,
You'll have to ride the rods."

THE MILL WAS MADE OF MARBLE

By JOE GLAZER

A song that came out of a bitter strike of April, 1947, at the Safie Textile Mill in Rockingham, North Carolina, by members of the Textile Workers' Union, CIO. An old striker, name apparently unknown, one day brought an eight-line poem to one of the Textile Workers' Union staff. It mentioned something about a "mill made of marble." Joe Glazer (no relation to the author) then fashioned a song based on the poem, and it later became very popular with union members.

I dreamed that I had died___ and gone to my re-ward,___ A job in Heav-en's tex-tile plant on a gold-en

bou - le - vard.

CHORUS

THE MILL WAS MADE OF

MAR-BLE, ____ The ma -chines were

made out of gold, ____ And

no - bod - y ev - er got

tired and no - bod - y

ev - er grew old. ____

This mill was built in a garden --
No dust or lint could be found.
The air was so fresh and so fragrant
With flowers and trees all around.

It was quiet and peaceful in heaven --
There was no clatter or boom.
You could hear the most beautiful music
As you worked at the spindle and loom.

There was no unemployment in heaven;
We worked steady all through the year;
We always had food for the children;
We never were haunted by fear.

When I woke from this dream about heaven
I wondered if someday there'd be
A mill like that one down below here on earth
For workers like you and like me.

MINER'S LIFEGUARD

A mining song based on the old hymn, "Life Is Like a Mountain Railroad." Coal operators would underweigh coal cars when the miners' pay used to depend on the weight of the coal that they mined, until the union instituted the use of checkers to check the weight.

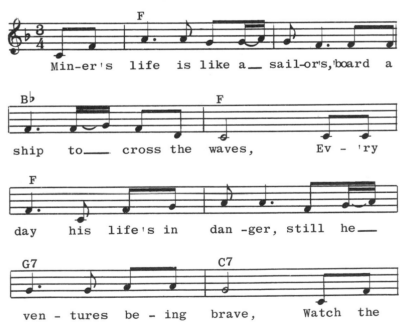

Min-er's life is like a— sail-or's, board a
ship to— cross the waves, Ev - 'ry
day his life's in dan -ger, still he—
ven - tures be - ing brave, Watch the

rocks, they're fall -ing dai - ly, care - less

min - ers____ al -ways fail, Keep your

hand up - on the dol - lar and your

eyes up - on the scale.

CHORUS

Un-ion min -ers, stand to-geth - er, heed no

op - er - a - tor's tales, Keep your

hand up - on the dol - lar, and your

eyes up - on the scale.

Soon this trouble will be ended
Union men will have their rights
After many years of bondage
Diggin' days and diggin' nights.
Then by honest weight we labor
Union workers never fail;
Keep your hand upon the dollar,
And your eyes upon the scales.

Let no union man be weakened
By newspapers false reports;
Be like sailors on the ocean
Trusting in their safe lifeboats.
Let your lifeboat be Jehovah
Those who trust him never fail,
Keep you hand upon the dollar,
And your eyes upon the scales.

MONSTER IN THE LOCH

A Scottish protest about the Polaris Missile Base at Holy (sic) Loch.

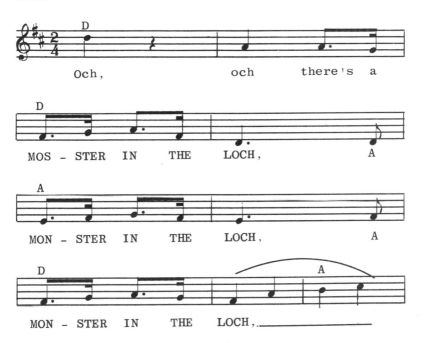

Och, och, there's a MON - STER IN THE LOCH and we din - na want Po - la - ris.

Och, och, we're off to Holy Loch,
Off to Holy Loch, we're off to Holy
　　　Loch,
Och, och, we're off to Holy Loch
And we dinna want Polaris.

The U.S.A. are giving subs away, etc.

Take them away, Papa L.B.J., etc.

Send the whole damn show up the
　　　Alamo, etc.

Suicide to have them in the
　　　Clyde, etc.

MRS. McGRATH

A fine broth of an Irish antiwar song, of folk origin—that is,
true folk origin, which means at least several generations old.

"Oh, MIS - SUS Mc - GRATH," the
Ser - geant said, "would you
like to make a sol - dier out of
your son Ted? With a
scar - let coat and a
big cocked hat, Now
MIS - SUS Mc - GRATH, would -n't
you like that?"

CHORUS

Wid yer too - ri - a,

fol - the did - dle - a,

Too- ri- oo- ri - oo - ri - a. Wid yer

too - ri - a, fol -the did -dle - a,

Too - ri - oo - ri - oo - ri - a.

So Mrs. McGrath lived on the seashore
For the space of seven long years or more,
Till she saw a big ship sailing into the bay,
"Hello, hello, I think 'tis he."

"Oh, Captain dear, where have you been?
Have you been sailing on the Mediterranean?
Oh, have you any tidings of my son Ted,
Is the poor boy living, or is he dead?"

Then up comes Ted without any legs
And in their place two wooden pegs.
She kissed him a dozen times or two,
Saying, "Holy Moses, it isn't you."

"Oh then were you drunk or were you blind
That you left your two fine legs behind?
Or was it walkin' upon the sea
Wore your two fine legs from the knees away?"

"Oh, Teddy me boy," the widow cried,
"Your two fine legs were your mama's pride.
I'd rather have my son as he used to be,
Than the King of France and his whole navee."

"All foreign wars I do proclaim,
Between Don John and the King of Spain,
By the heavens I'll make them rue the time,
That they swept the legs from a child of mine.

'Oh, then if I had you back again,
I'd never let you go to fight the King of Spain,
For I'd rather my Ted as he used to be
Than the King of Spain and his whole navy."

MURDER ON THE ROAD IN ALABAMA

By LEN H. CHANDLER, JR.

A graphic modern ballad whose words tell the story pungently.

fight -ing for what's right, if you're —

black or if you're white, you're a

tar - get in the night in Al - a -

bam - a.

Oh we marched right by that spot in Alabama, (2)
Oh we marched right by that spot
Where the coward fired the shots
Where the Klansman fired the shots in Alabama.

Oh we know who is to blame in Alabama (2)
She caught two bullets in the brain
Before we learned to say her name
And George Wallace is the shame of Alabama.

Deep within the sovereign state of Alabama (2)
Deep within the sovereign state
There's a poison pit of hate,
And George Wallace is the heart of Alabama

There's a man behind the guns of Alabama (2)
There's a man behind the guns
Kills for hate, for fear, for fun,
And George Wallace is top gun of Alabama.

It was Jackson on the roads of Alabama,
It was Reeb on the roads of Alabama,
William Moore's been dead and gone
But this killing still goes on,
Now Liuzzo's on the road in Alabama.

232

There's a movement on the road in Alabama,
There's a movement on the road in Alabama,
Blcak man, white man, Christian, Jew
We've got to keep on marching through
Oh the tyrant days are few in Alabama.

It was murder on the road in Alabama . . .

MY CHILDREN ARE SEVEN IN NUMBER

A song that rose out of the bitter mine strikes in the towns of
Davidson and Wilder, Tennessee, in 1933. Barney Graham
was a mountaineer mine-workers' leader who was shot in the
back by a thug imported by the mine owners from Chicago.
The tune is from "My Bonnie Lies Over the Ocean."

MY   CHIL –DREN   ARE   SEV – EN   IN

NUM– BER, _____   We   have   to   sleep

four   in   a   bed, _____   I'm

strik – ing   with   my   fel – low

work – ers _____   to   get   them   more

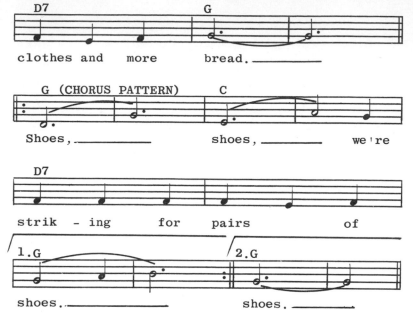

clothes and more bread.

G (CHORUS PATTERN)   **C**

Shoes, _____ shoes, _____ we're

D7

strik - ing for pairs of

1.G   **2.G**

shoes. _____ shoes. _____

Pellagra is cramping my stomach,
My wife is sick with T.B.;
My babies are starving for sweet milk,
Oh, there's so much sickness for me.
Milk, milk, we're striking for gallons
 of milk, etc.

I'm needing a shave and a haircut,
The barbers I cannot afford;
My wife cannot wash without soapsuds,
And she had to borrow a board.
Soap, Soap, we're striking for bars
 of soap, etc.

My house is a shack on the hillside,
Its floors are unpainted and bare;
I haven't a screen to my windows,
And carbide cans do for a chair.
Homes, homes, we're striking for
 better homes, etc.

Oh, Aid Truck go over the mountain,
Oh, Aid Truck come back with a load;
For we are just getting a dollar
A few days a month on the road.
Gas, gas, we're bumming a gallon of gas, etc.

They shot Barney Graham our leader,
His spirit abides with us still;
The spirit of strength for justice,
No bullets have the power to kill.
Barney, Barney, we're thinking of you
        today, etc.

Oh, miners, go on with the union,
Oh, miners, go on with the fight;
For we're in the struggle for justice
And we're in the struggle for right.
Justice, justice, we're striking for
        justice for all, etc.

MY SWEETHEART'S THE MULE IN THE MINES

Mules are no longer found in mines, which are now electrified, but in the old days boys of 12 to 15 years of age would drive them without reins, cussing and shouting all the way. The tune is based on an 1890's melody, "My Sweetheart's the Man in the Moon."

MY   SWEET-HEART'S THE   MULE   IN   THE   MINES, _____   I   drive   her   with-out   an-y   lines, _____   On   the   bump-er   I   sit,   and   I

chew and I spit all o - ver my

sweet-heart's be - hind. _____

MY WIFE HAD A BABY

First time in print. I collected it one afternoon between rehearsals from Frederick O'Neal, author and official at Actors' Equity, who told me he used to hear it sung by track-lining railroad workers in the South.

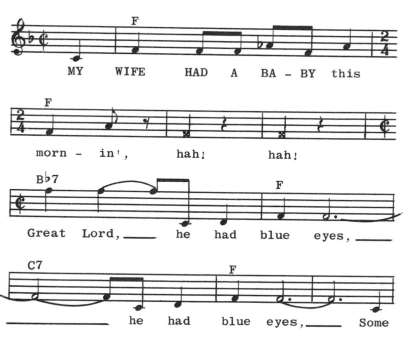

MY WIFE HAD A BA - BY this

morn - in', hah! hah!

Great Lord, ___ he had blue eyes, ___

___ he had blue eyes, ___ Some

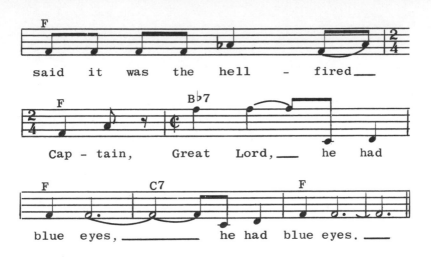

said it was the hell - fired___

Cap - tain, Great Lord, ___ he had

blue eyes, _____ he had blue eyes. ___

NEVER TOO MUCH LOVE

Another Chicago Freedom Movement song by the same writers as "Keep On Pushing," and also recorded by the Impressions.

CHORUS

Too much love, _ too much love,___

Nev - er in this world will there be

1. too much love. ___ 2. too much love. ___

VERSE

I like to drink whis -key, I

I don't know but I think I'm right,
Folks in heaven both black and white.
I don't know but I've been told,
Folks in heaven won't tell me where
    to go.

Too much hate, too much hate,
Always in this world there is too
    much hate.
Too much war, too much war,
Always in this world there is too
    much war.

War is sad, war is long,
Everybody knows that war is wrong,
People tired, people sore,
People just want to end the war.

People in Mississippi thrown off
    their land,
Even the government won't give a
    hand.
But the Movement stays on and on,
People are living on hope and a song.

If religion were a thing that money
        could buy,
The rich would live and the poor would
        die,
But I thank my god it is not so
Both the rich and poor together must go.

Some people are good, some people
    are bad,
Some people are happy, some people
    are sad,
Some people are black, some people
    are white,
But we're all together in the human
    plight.

They say the Movement is a non-violent
    thing
Led by people like Martin Luther King,
I want my freedom, and I want it now,
Join with us and we will show you how.

A NEW JERUSALEM

Words by WILLIAM BLAKE;
music by SIR C. HUBERT PARRY

William Blake's (1757-1827) beautiful poem expressing his horror at the excesses of the British Industrial Revolution, later set to music by Sir C. Hubert Parry (1848-1918). This music was recently used satirically as part of the background score in the fine British film *Loneliness of the Long Distance Runner*.

And did those feet in an - cient__ time walk up -on Eng-land's moun- tains green? And was the Ho - ly Lamb of __ God on Eng-land's pleas- ant pas - tures seen? And did the coun - te -nance di - vine shine forth up - on our cloud - ed

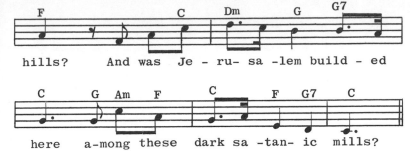

hills? And was Je - ru- sa -lem build - ed

here a-mong these dark sa -tan- ic mills?

And did the countenance divine
Shine forth upon our clouded hills?
And was Jerusalem builded here
Among these dark satanic mills?

Bring me my bow of burning gold!
Bring me my arrows of desire!
Bring me my spear! O clouds, unfold!
Bring me my chariot of fire!

I will not cease from mental fight,
Nor shall my sword sleep in my hand,
Till we have built Jerusalem
In England's green and pleasant land.

900 MILES

Woody Guthrie sang this with Cisco Houston. Another version of the song, minus 400 of the 900 miles, was a hit song in the 1960s, started by Hedy West.

I am rid- ing on this train, there are

tears in___ my eyes,

Well, this train I ride on
Is a hundred coaches long,
You can hear the whistle blow a hundred miles,
And the lonesome whistle call
Is mournfullest of all,
'Cause it's NINE HUNDRED MILES from my home.

Well, I'll pawn my watch and I'll
Pawn you my chain,
I'll pawn you my gold diamond ring,
For if this train runs me right,
I'll be home Saturday night,
'Cause I'm NINE HUNDRED MILES from my home.

NO IRISH NEED APPLY

Words by J. T. POOLE

When thousands of Irish immigrants came to this country in
the middle 1840s during the Great Potato Famine in Ireland,
the title of this song was a not uncommon sign in newspaper
ads and in places of employment. One hundred twenty-five
years later, John F. Kennedy became the first Irish-American
President of the United States. It may be salutary for us all to
be reminded of this fact occasionally. The song was written
in the 1860s. The "Tribune" of the second verse might very
likely have been Horace Greeley's newspaper of New York,
later the *Herald Tribune*. "*Milia murther*" is a Gaelic phrase
that means "a thousand murders."

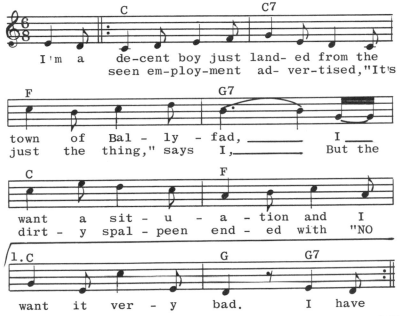

I'm a de-cent boy just land- ed from the
seen em-ploy-ment ad- ver-tised,"It's

town of Bal - ly - fad, _____ I ____
just the thing," says I,_____ But the

want a sit - u - a - tion and I
dirt - y spal - peen end - ed with "NO

1.C
want it ver - y bad. I have

243

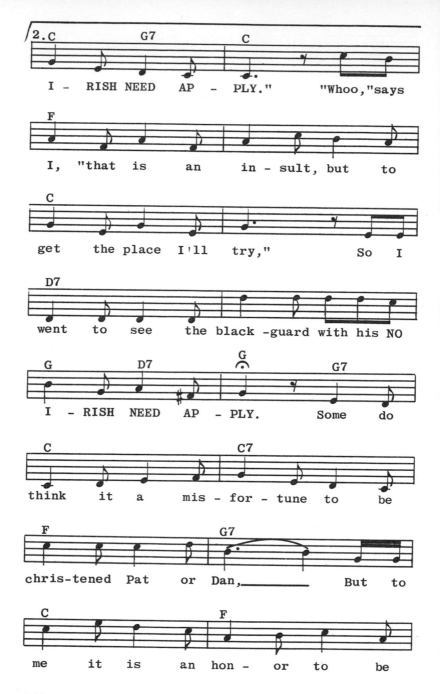

born   an   I - rish - man.

```
        I started out to find the house,
        I got there mighty soon,
        I found the old chap seated,
        He was reading the Tribune.
        I told him what I came for,
        When he in a rage did fly,
        "No!" he says, "You are a Paddy,
        And NO IRISH NEED APPLY."
        Then I gets my dander rising,
        And I'd like to black his eye,
        For to tell an Irish gentleman
        "NO IRISH NEED APPLY."

        I couldn't stand it longer
        So a-hold of him I took,
        And I gave him such a beating
        As he'd get at Donnybrook.
        He hollered, "Milia Murther,"
        And to get away did try,
        And swore he'd never write again,
        "NO IRISH NEED APPLY."
        Well, he made a big apology,
        I told him then goodbye, saying,
        "When next you want a beating, write
        NO IRISH NEED APPLY!"
```

NO MAN CAN FIND THE WAR

By TIM BUCKLEY and LARRY BECKETT

Tim Buckley, a co-writer of this song, is currently one of
our more interesting and important younger folksingers, if he
doesn't mind being called such, since at this writing I am told
that the term "folksinger" isn't very "commercial."

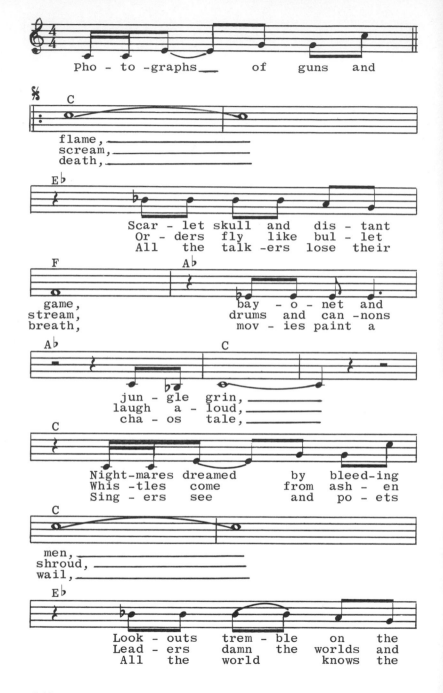

shore,
roar,
score,

But NO MAN____

CAN FIND THE WAR. ____

1.C

Tape re - cord - ers ech - o

2.F

Is the war a - cross the

sea? Is the war be - hind the

sky? Have you each and all____

____ gone blind? ____

Is the war in- side your

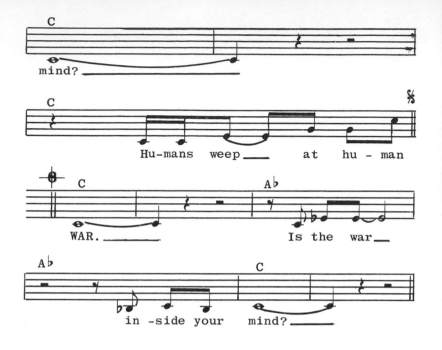

NO MORE AUCTION BLOCK FOR ME

This may have been written to honor Lincoln's Emancipation Proclamation, 1863, the "Year of Jubilo." It was sung by black soldiers of the North, ex-slaves.

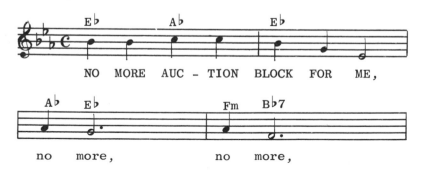

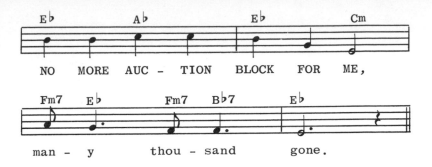

NO MORE AUC - TION BLOCK FOR ME,

man - y thou - sand gone.

No more driver's lash for me,
No more, no more!
No more driver's lash for me;
Many thousand gone.

No more peck of corn for me,
No more, no more!
No more peck of corn for me;
Many thousand gone.

No more pint of salt for me,
No more, no more!
No more pint of salt for me;
Many thousand gone.

O FREEDOM

The great old spiritual with new freedom verses. Although a spiritual in style, it was used as a marching song by Negro regiments in the Civil War. The original song in various versions is still sung widely today.

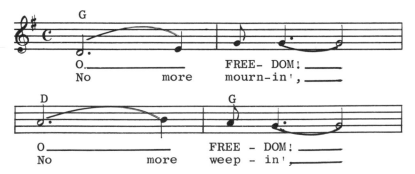

O._____ FREE- DOM! _____
No   more   mourn-in', _____

O._____ FREE - DOM! _____
No   more   weep - in', _____

O._____ FREE- DOM o - ver
No more mis - 'ry o - ver

me!_____ Here and now) And be -
me!_____

fore I'd be a slave, I'd be

bur - ied in my grave! And go

home to my Lord and be

free!_____

No more conformin' . . .

Free to be honest . . .

Free to make new things . . .

Free to be me . . .

No more violence . . .

OH, MY LIVER AND MY LUNGS

"Lights" is the old-fashioned word for "innards." At first blush this song seems like a corny mining song; but it is a genuine, moving plaint by a miner who is in actual physical pain.

OH, MY LIV - ER AND MY LUNGS, my lights and my legs, they're pain - ing me, they're pain - ing me, My heart is sad, my head is bad and I think I'm go - ing cra - zy. Crushed___ by the days of___

end - less   toil   and   sleep - less

nights   of   woe,_____   There is

naught   but   an - guish__

ev - 'ry - where   As   on   through

life   we   go.

Now maybe someday I'll reach that higher goal,
I know I can make it with just a little bit
    of soul,
'Cause I've got my strength, and it don't make
    sense
Not to KEEP PUSHING ON.

Look-a, look-a yonder, what's that I see
A great big stone standing there ahead of me.
But I've got my strength, and it don't make sense
Not to KEEP ON PUSHING.

OH, WALLACE

A tremendous song from the Selma, Alabama, Freedom Movement. It is really an inspired effort, and its great impact can be
appreciated only by hearing it sung by the people of that locale
on a recording made in the field called "Freedom Songs, Selma,
Alabama," on the Folkways label.

CHORUS

OH,_____ WAL - LACE,_____ you

nev -er can jail us all,_____

OH, WAL -LACE,___

se - gre - ga - tion's bound to fall,_

da dat____ da da da

dat, da da da da da

dat, da dat,___ da da da dat.

(VERSE)

I said I read in the

I read in the paper just the other day
The Freedom Fighters, they were on their way,
They're coming by bus and airplane too
They'll even walk if you ask them to.

Don't you worry about going to jail
'Cause Martin Luther King will go your bail.
He'll get you out right on time,
Put you back on the picket line.

I don't want no mess, I don't want no jive,
And I want my freedom in Sixty-five,
Listen, Jim Clark, you can hear this plea,
You can lock us in the house,
You can throw away the key.

Now, I'm no preacher, but I can tell
You've got to straighten up
Or you're bound for hell,
You can tell Wilson Baker and Al Lingo
That the people in Selma won't take no mo'.

Well this is the message I want you to hear,
You know I want my freedom
And I want it this year,
So you can tell Jim Clark
And all those state guys too,
I'm gonna have my freedom
And there's nothing they can do.

You can push me around, you can throw me away,
But I still want my freedom
And I want it every day.
You can tell Jim Clark and Al Lingo
It's time for them to end Jim Crow.

Route Eighty is the way we'll come,
I know them boys will have a lot of fun.
You might see black, and a few whites too,
They're looking for freedom like me and you.

I saw James Orange just the other day,
He was getting ready to be on his way.
He had a white shirt on and some blue jeans,
Just come on to Eighty, you'll see what we mean.

You know Jack and Jill went up the hill
And Jill came down with the Civil Rights Bill.
Don't want no shuckin', don't want no jive,
Gonna get my freedom in sixty-five.

THE OLD REBEL SOLDIER

A passionate protest by Innes Randolph, a major in the Confederate Army. It was originally set to the tune of "Joe Bowers," but this melody was collected by Frank Warner in North Carolina.

hate   the   pi - zen   Yan - kees   and   I

fit   'em   all   I   cud.

I followed old Marse Robert
For about four years nigh,
Got wounded at Manassas and
Starved at Point Lookout.
I cotched the rheumatism from
Fightin' in the snow,
But I kilt a chanct o' Yankees--
And I wish I'd kilt some mo'.

Three hundred thousand Yankees
Are stiff in Southern dust,
We got three hundred thousand
Before they conquered us,
They died of Southern fever--
And Southern steel and shot,
And wisht we'd a-got three million
Instead of what we got.

I hate the Yankee nation
And the uniform of blue,
I hate the regulations
Of this great republic too,
I hate the Freedmen's Bureau
With all its mess and fuss--
Oh, the thievin', lyin' Yankees--
I hate 'em wuss and wuss.

I can't take up my musket
To fight 'em any mo',
But I ain't gonna love 'em--
And that is sartain sho',
And I don't want no pardon
For what I've done or am,
And I won't be reconstructed
AND I DO NOT GIVE A DAMN!

ONE MAN'S HANDS

Words by ALEX COMFORT; music by PETE SEEGER

Another fine song written by the British doctor, Alex Comfort. In one songbook containing this number appears the following parenthetical remark at the end: "And so on, for as many good causes as time permits."

ONE MAN'S HANDS can't break a pris-on down, _____ Two man's hands can't break a pris-on down, _____ But if two and two and fif-ty make a mil-lion, we'll see that day come round, we'll see that day come round. _____

One man's voice can't shout to make them hear,
Two men's voices can't shout to make them hear,
But if two and fifty make a million
We'll see that day come 'round,
We'll see that day come 'round.

One man's strength can't ban the atom bomb, etc.

One man's strength can't break the color bar, etc.

One man's strength can't make the union roll, etc.

One man's feet can't walk around the land, etc.

One man's eyes can't see the way ahead, etc.

ON THE PICKET LINE

There are numerous parodies sung on picket lines, or new words to old tunes. "Polly, Wolly Doodle" served as the tune for this famous picket-line song, heard first in the 1920s.

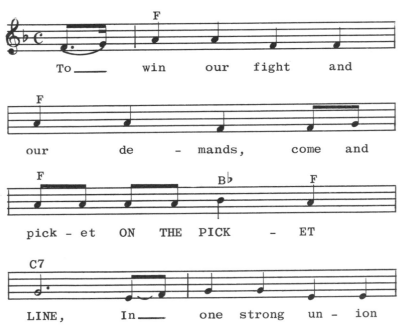

If you've never spent a night in jail,
Come and picket on the picket line;
You will be invited without fail,
Come and picket on the picket line.

CHORUS:
    On the line, on the line,
    On the picket, picket line,
    The dirty little scab,
    We will use him like a rag,
    Come and picket ON THE PICKET LINE.

If you don't like scabs and thugs and stools,
Come and picket on the picket line,
For you show the boss that the worker rules,
When you picket on the picket line.

CHORUS:
    On the line, on the line,
    On the picket, picket line,
    All together take a hike,
    And we'll surely win the strike,
    Come and picket ON THE PICKET LINE.

PARTISAN'S SONG (PARTIZANER HYMNE, or LIED)

A song very popular among Yiddish-speaking people all over
the world. The words are presumably by Hirsch Glick, and the
music by the Pokrass brothers. A great deal of investigation
has failed to unearth any more than that about its background,
time of writing, or the author of these English lyrics, although
others exist. It has a martial and defiant air, but in light of the
history of the Jews in the past thirty-five years, the song has an
underlying element of profound pathos.

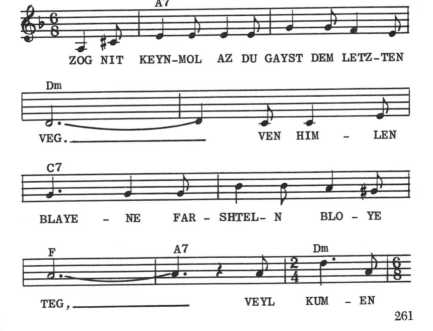

ZOG NIT KEYN-MOL AZ DU GAYST DEM LETZ-TEN

VEG._____   VEN HIM – LEN

BLAYE – NE FAR – SHTEL- N BLO – YE

TEG,_____   VEYL KUM – EN

Fun grinem palmenland biz land fun vaysen shney,
Mir kumen un mit undzer payn, mit undzer vey;
Un voo gefalen iz a shpritz fun undzer blut,
Shpritzen vet dort undzer gvure, undzer mut.

Es vet di morgenzun bagilden undz dem haynt,
Un der nechten vet farshvinden mitn faynt;
Nor oyb farzamen vet di zun in dem ka-yor,
Vi a parol zol geyn dos leed fun door tzu door.

Geshriben iz dos leed mit blut und nit mit bly,
S'iz nit keyn leedl fun a foygel oyf der fry;
Dos hut a folk tzvishen falendi-ke vent,
Dos leed gezungen mit naganes in di hant.

Zog nit keyn mol az du gayst dem letzten veg,
Ven himlen blayene farshteln bloye teg;
Kumen vet noch undzer oysgebente shuh,
Es vet a poyk tun undzer trot -- mir zaynen do!

TRANSLATION:

Never say that there is only death for you,
Though leaden skies may be
Concealing days of blue,
Because the hour we have hungered for is near,
Beneath our tread the earth shall tremble,
We are here!

From land of palm tree to the
Far-off land of snow,
We shall be coming with our torment and our woe,
And everywhere our blood has sunk into the earth,
Shall our bravery, our vigor blossom forth.

We'll have the morning sun to set our day aglow,
And all our yesterdays shall vanish with the foe,
And if the time is long before the sun appears,
Then let this song go
Like a signal through the years.

This song was written with
Blood and not with lead,
It's not a sing that summer birds sing overhead,
It was a people among toppling barrivades,
That sang this song of ours
With pistols and grenades.

Never say that there is only death for you,
Though leaden skies may be concealing days of blue,
Because the hour we have hungered for is near,
Beneath our tread the earth shall tremble,
We are here!

PEACE MARCH SONG

By JERRY ATINSKY

Marching has become a standard protest activity. It probably stems from Ghandi's non-violent efforts against British rule in India in the 1930s, and is often a most effective weapon.

C
Two by two we walk a - long,

C6   G7
From our lips a peace - ful song,

G7
On and on un - til the end,

G7   C
With each step a new - found friend.

F (CHORUS)
There's a mush - room cloud on high, ____

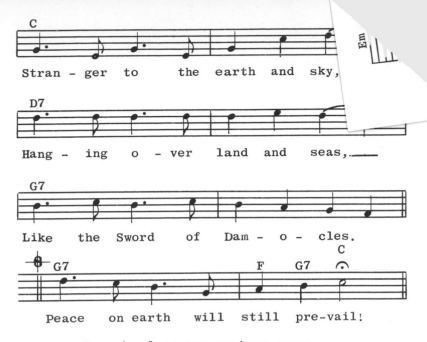

Stran - ger to the earth and sky,

Hang - ing o - ver land and seas,____

Like the Sword of Dam - o - cles.

Peace on earth will still pre-vail!

Four by four our numbers grow,
Proudly marching row by row,
As we sing out loud and clear,
All our fears will disappear.

Ten by ten we multiply,
From our lips a fervent cry,
"We shall win, we shall not fail."
Peace on earth will still prevail!

THE PEATBOG SOLDIERS

The first concentration camp song to make a powerful impression on the world in the 1930s, this was supposedly written in the Boergernoor Concentration Camp in Germany. It was first actually sung in the camp because the words were apparently non-political, though it was later forbidden.

Far and wide as the

eye can wan - der heath and bog are ev - 'ry - where,

Not a bird sings out to cheer us, oaks are stand - ing gaunt and bare.

CHORUS
We are the PEAT - BOG SOL - DIERS, we're march - ing with our spades to the bog. _____

Up and down the guards are pacing,
No one, no one can go through.
Flight would mean a sure death facing,
Guns and barbed wire greet our view. (Cho.)

But for us there is no complaining,
Winter will in time be past;
One day we shall cry rejoicing,
"Homeland dear, you're mine at last."

LAST CHORUS:
Then will the peat-bog soldiers
March no more with their spades to the bog!
Then will the peat-bog soldiers
March no more with their spades to the bog!

POLLUTION

By TOM LEHRER

Tom Lehrer writes some of the most effective funny songs in the world—about serious situations. His melodies are a charming distillation of the lighter compositions of the classical composers, plus a dash of Sir Arthur Sullivan, along with his own deft accompaniments on the piano. And finally, that indescribable voice with its overtones of nasality, throatiness, intellectual New Yorkese, and undertones of a very high Intelligence Quotient. My name is at times confused with his, which I number among the higher of compliments.

Calypso

If you vis - it A - mer - i - can cit - y,

you will find ____ it

ver - y pret - ty,

Just two things ____ of which you

must be - ware: ____

Don't drink the wa - ter and don't ____

____ breathe the air. POL -

LU - TION, ____ POL - LU - TION, ____ They got

smog and sew - age and mud,

Turn on___ your tap and___ get hot and cold___ run-ning crud.

slaugh - ter,___ They're drink - ing___ the wa - ter___ and breath- ing (cough.....) the air.___

See the halibuts and the sturgeons
Being wiped out by detergeons,
Fish gotta swim and birds gotta fly,
But they don't last long if they try.
POLLUTION, POLLUTION,
You can use the latest toothpaste,
And then rinse your mouth with industrial waste.

Just go out for a breath of air,
And you'll be ready for Medicare,
The city streets are really quite a thrill,
If the hoods don't get you, monoxide will.
POLLUTION, POLLUTION,
Wear a gas mask and a veil,
Then you can breath long as you don't inhale.

269

Lots of things that you can drink,
But stay away from the kitchen sink,
Throw out your breakfast garbage
And I've got a hunch
That folks downstream will drink it for lunch.
So go to the city, see the crazy people there,
Like lambs to the *slaughter, they're
Drinking the water and breathing
(cough.........) the air.

THE PREACHER AND THE SLAVE
(PIE IN THE SKY)

Words by JOE HILL

Joe Hill's most successful song, along with Casey Jones. Joe Hill, was, of course, the IWW (Wobbly) bard who was framed on a murder charge and executed. (See the song "Joe Hill" in this book.)

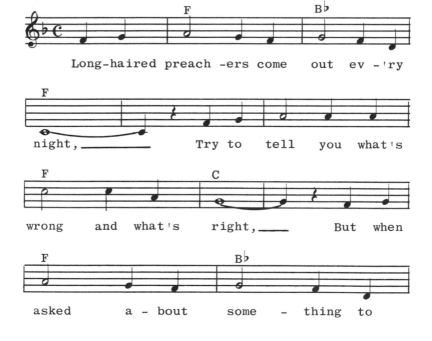

Long-haired preach -ers come out ev -'ry night,_____ Try to tell you what's wrong and what's right,____ But when asked a - bout some - thing to

eat, _____ They will an-swer with
voic - es so sweet: _____

CHORUS
"You will eat_____ bye and
(You will eat)

bye, _____ In that
(bye and bye)

glo - ri - ous land in the

sky, _____ Work and
(way up high)

pray, _____ live on
(work and pray)

hay, _____ You'll get
(live on hay)

pie   in   the   sky   when you

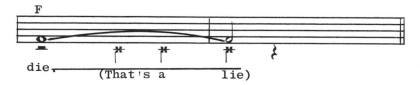

die.   (That's a   lie)

And the starvation army they play,
And they sing and they clap and they pray,
Till they get all your coin on the drum --
Then they tell you when you're on the bum:

If you fight hard for children and wife --
Try to get something good in this life --
You're a sinner and bad man, they tell;
When you die you will sure go to Hell.

Working men of all countries, unite!
Side by side we for freedom will fight.
When the world and its wealth we have gained,
To the grafters we'll sing this refrain:

LAST CHORUS

You will eat (you will eat)
Bye and bye, (bye and bye)
When you've learned how to
Cook and to fry (way up high)
Chop some wood (chop some wood)
'Twill do you good (do you good)
And you'll eat in the sweet
Bye and bye (that's no lie)

THE REUBEN JAMES (THE SINKING OF)

By WOODIE GUTHRIE

A great Woody Guthrie song written before we were in the war as the result of the sinking of the first American ship by a German submarine. The cry, "Tell me, what were their names" rings out like the angel Gabriel about to call the roll, and is so touching because most soldiers and sailors die with such unremitting anonymity.

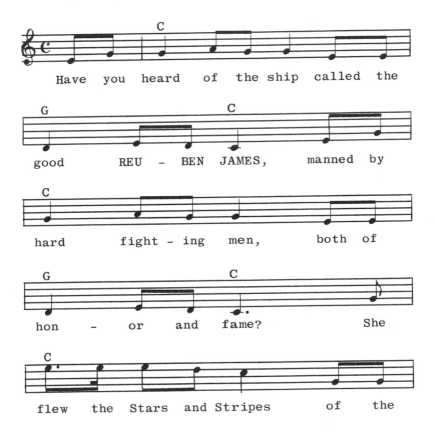

Have you heard of the ship called the good REU - BEN JAMES, manned by hard fight - ing men, both of hon - or and fame? She flew the Stars and Stripes of the

Land of the Free, but to-night she's in her grave on the bot - tom of the sea.

CHORUS

Tell me, what were their names, Tell me, what were their names? Did you have a friend on the

1.C

good REU - BEN JAMES? Tell me,

2.C

good REU - BEN JAMES?

It was there in the dark
Of that uncertain night
That we watched for the U-boat
And waited for a fight,
Then a whine and a rock
And a great explosion roar,
And they laid the REUBEN JAMES
On the cold ocean floor.

Now tonight there are lights
In our country so bright,
In the farms and the cities
They are telling of this fight,
And now our mighty battleships
Will steam the bounding main,
And remember the name of the
Good REUBEN JAMES.

THE REVEL

Words by BARTHOLOMEW DOWLING

An absolutely fascinating and brilliant song that I learned twenty-odd years ago from Shana Ager Alexander, recently of *Life* magazine and now editor-in-chief of *McCall's*. She learned it from her father, the famous popular songwriter, Milton Ager, and her mother Cecilia Ager, the writer. All of them learned it from Dorothy Parker, who was not noted for her bell-like voice, and God only knows where she learned it. The words are by an Irish poet, Bartholomew Dowling (1823-1863), who lived in this country for a while. It refers to the numerous plagues in India, either cholera or malaria, possibly around 1836.

Collected and arranged by Tom Glazer, © 1967, Songs Music, Inc., Scarborough, N.Y. All rights reserved.

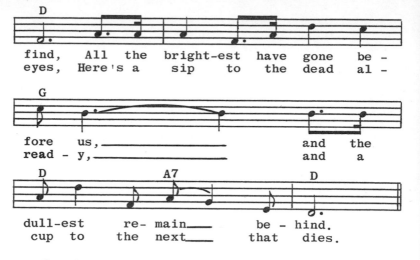

find, All the bright-est have gone be -
eyes, Here's a sip to the dead al -

fore us, _____ and the
read - y, _____ and a

dull-est re- main___ be - hind.
cup to the next___ that dies.

3. We meet 'neath the sounding rafter
   And the walls all around are bare
   And the dead echo back our laughter
   For they know that we'll soon be there.

4. So, stand to your glasses steady
   This world is a world of lies
   Here's a sip to the dead already
   And a cup to the next that dies.

THE RICH MAN AND THE POOR MAN

A parody of an old English carol based on the Biblical parable
of Dives, a rich man, and Lazarus, a poor man. This parody
first appeared in, and was made popular by, a songbook put
out by the Brookwood Labor College of Katonah, New York,
in the 1920s.

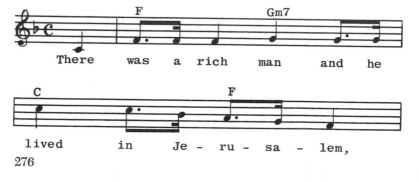

There was a rich man and he

lived in Je - ru - sa - lem,

Glo - ry hal - le - lu - jah,

hi - ro - je - rum, He

wore a silk hat and his

coat was ver - y spru - ci - um,

Glo - ry hal - le - lu - jah,

hi - ro - je - rum.

F (CHORUS)

Hi - ro - je - rum,

hi - ro - je - rum,

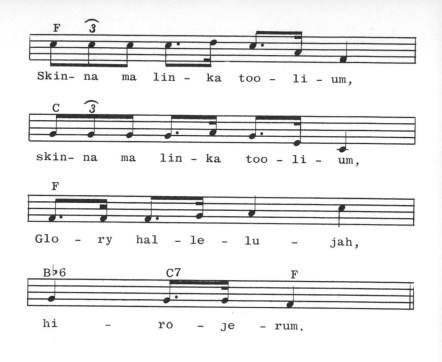

Skin- na ma lin - ka too - li - um,

skin- na ma lin - ka too - li - um,

Glo - ry hal - le - lu - jah,

hi - ro - je - rum.

One day to his door there came a human wreckium,
Glory hallelujah, hi-ro-jerum,
He wore a bowler hat and the
Brim was round his neckium,
Glory hallelujah, hi-ro-jerum.

The poor man begger for a
Piece of bread and cheesium,
Glory hallelujah, hi-ro-jerum,
The rich man said he'd call for a policium,
Glory hallelujah, hi-ro-jerum.

The poor man died and his soul went to Heavium,
Glory hallelujah, hi-ro-jerum,
He danced with the angels till a
Quarter past elevium,
Glory hallelujah, hi-ro-jerum.

The rich man died but he didn't fare so wellium,
Glory hallelujah, hi-ro-jerum,
He couldn't get to Heaven
So he had to go to Hellium,
Glory hallelujah, hi-ro-jerum.

The moral of this story is: Ricjes are no jokium,
Glory hallelujah, hi-ro-jerum,
We'll all go to Heaven
'Cause we're all stony brokium,
Glory hallelujah, hi-ro-jerum.

THE RISING OF THE MOON

The great Irish freedom song often sung by the Clancy Brothers.

(Tune:Wearing of the Green)

Oh,then tell me,Sean O'-Far-rell,tell me
why you hur - ry so? Hush, me
dar - lin', hush and lis -ten, and his
cheeks were all a - glow. I hear
or - ders from the Cap -tain, get you
read - y quick and soon, For the

pikes must be to - geth -er by THE

RIS - ING OF THE MOON.

CHORUS

By THE RIS - ING OF THE MOON, By THE

RIS - ING OF THE MOON, For the

pikes must be to - geth-er by THE

RIS - ING OF THE MOON.

Oh, then tell me, Sean O'Farrell,
Where the gathering is to be,
In the old spot by the river,
Right well known to you and me.
One more word for signal token,
Whistle up the marching tune,
With your pike upon your shoulder
By THE RISING OF THE MOON.

Out of many a mid wall cabin,
Eyes were watching through the night,
Many a manly heart was throbbing,
For the coming morning light.
Murmers ran along the valley,
Like the banshee's lonely croon,
And a thousand pikes were flashing
By THE RISING OF THE MOON.

There beside the singing river,
That dark mass of men were seen,
Far above their shining weapons,
Hung their own beloved green.
Death to every foe and traitor,
Forward strike the marching tune,
And hurrah, me boys, for freedom,
'Tis THE RISING OF THE MOON.

ROLL THE UNION ON

The melody is based on a gospel hymn, "Roll the Chariot On,"
and is one of the must popular of all union songs. It was written
in 1936 at a labor school in Arkansas; an organizer named John
Handcox wrote the first verse, while others were written by
Lee Hays, then of the Almanac Singers and later of the Weavers.

With a steady beat

We're gon - na roll, ___ we're gon- na
roll, ___ we're gon-na ROLL THE UN - ION
ON, We're gon-na roll, ___ we're gon- na

If the scab is in the way
We're gonna roll it over him,
We're gonna roll it over him,
We're gonna roll it over him,
If the scab is in the way
We're gonna roll it over him,
We're gonna ROLL THE UNION ON!

```
If the sheriff's in the way
We're gonna roll it over him,
We're gonna roll it over him,
We're gonna roll it over him,
If the sheriff's in the way
We're gonna roll it over him,
We're gonna ROLL THE UNION ON!

Whoever's in the way
We're gonna roll it over him,
We're gonna roll it over him,
We're gonna roll it over him,
Whoever's in the way
We're gonna roll it over him,
We're gonna ROLL THE UNION ON!
```

THE SCABS CRAWL IN

For obvious reasons, the dirtiest word to a union man, especially a beleaguered one, is "scab," because scabs break strikes and break unions, directly or indirectly. This ditty, hardly substantial enough to be called a song, though very popular, is a parody of "The Worms Crawl In."

THE SCABS CRAWL IN and the scabs crawl out, They crawl in un - der and all a - bout, They

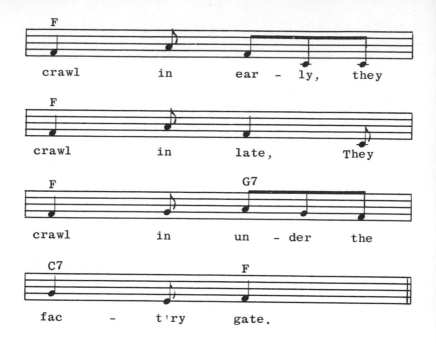

crawl in ear - ly, they

crawl in late, They

crawl in un - der the

fac - t'ry gate.

SHALOM CHAVERIM

Succinct, brief, powerful. An import from Israel. Israelis (and Arabs) say "hello" the best way—they say "Shalom"—Peace. The English words are mine.

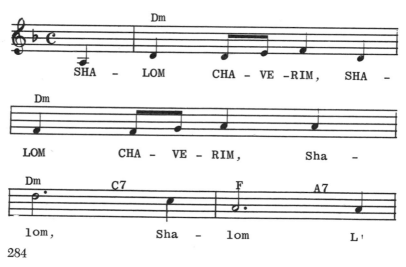

SHA - LOM CHA - VE -RIM, SHA -

LOM CHA - VE - RIM, Sha -

lom, Sha - lom L'

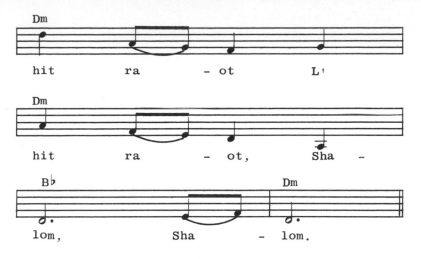

hit   ra   - ot   L'

hit   ra   - ot,   Sha -

lom,   Sha   - lom.

Shalom, fellow men,
Till we meet again,
Shalom means peace
Till we meet again.
Shalom, fellow men,
Shalom means peace.

SI ME QUIERES ESCRIBIR

A great, passionate outcry of the Spanish Civil War.

SI ME   QUIE- RES ES - CRI - BIR,

Ya   sa - bes me pa - ra -der - o,

SI   ME

QUIE-RES ES - CRI - BIR, Ya sa - bes me pa - ra - der - o en el fren - te de Gan - de - sa pri - me - ra li - nea de fue - go, En el fren- te de Gan - de - sa pri - me - ra li -nea de fue - go.

Si tu quieres comer bien
Barato y de buena forma
En el frente de Gandesa
Alli tienen una fonda. . .

En la entrada de la fonda
Hay un moro Mojama
Que te dice, "Pasa, pasa
Que quieres para comer. . ."

El primer plato que dan
Son grenadas rompedoras
El segundo de matralla
Para recordar memorias. . .

If you want to eat your fill,
Good food and not too many pesos,
On that bloody battlefield
Stands an inn where you are welcome.

At the entrance of this inn there
Waits a Moor by name Mohammed,
Who warmly greets you, "Hurry, hurry,
Rare and spicy food awaits you."

The first dish which they serve
Is hot grenades in quick succession,
Followed by a burst of shrapnel,
Makes a meal you'll all remember.

SIXTEEN TONS

By MERLE TRAVIS

Merle Travis wrote this song out of his own family background. His father, a miner, was always in debt to the mining company store, so much so that he never had any real money but had to use tokens at the store. His father used to say, "I can't afford to die; I owe my soul to the company store."

With a driving beat

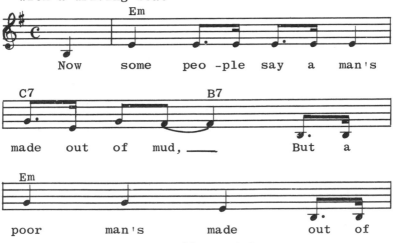

Now   some   peo-ple   say   a   man's

made   out   of   mud, ___   But   a

poor   man's   made   out   of

© 1947, American Music Co. Used by permission.

Pe - ter, don't you call me 'cause

I can't go, _____ I

owe my soul to the

com - pa - ny store.

I was born one morning when the sun didn't shine,
I picked up my shovel and I walked to the mine,
I loaded sixteen tons of number nine coal,
And the straw boss hollered,
"Well, bless my soul!"

I was born one morning in the drizzling rain;
Fighting and trouble is my middle name.
I was raised in the bottoms by a momma hound --
I'm mean as a dog but I'm gentle as a lamb.

If you see me coming, you better step aside,
A lot of men didn't, and a lot of men died,
I got a fist of iron and a fist of steel,
If the right one don't get you
Then the left one will.

SOUP SONG

The melody is "My Bonnie Lies Over the Ocean," and the words
come from the picket lines of the 1930s, or perhaps from the
soup and bread lines of mission societies. It is another example,
frequently encountered in the U.S., of humorous songs written about extremely unhumorous situations.

I'm spend-ing my nights at the

flop-house, _____ I'm spend -ing my

days on the street, _____ I'm

look - ing for work and I

find none, _____ I wish I had

some - thing to eat. _____

SOUP, _____

SOUP, _____ They give me a

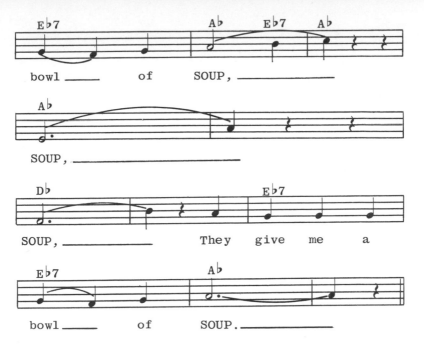

bowl ____ of SOUP, _____

SOUP, _____

SOUP, _____ They give me a

bowl ____ of SOUP. _____

I spent twenty years in the factory,
I did everything I was told.
They said I was loyal and faithful,
Now even before I get old:

I saved fifteen bucks with my banker
To buy me a car and a yacht.
I went down to draw out my fortune,
And this was the answer I got:

I fought in the war for my country,
I went out to bleed and to die.
I thought that my country would help me,
But this was my country's reply:

THE STARVING CHILD (WPA LULLABY)

By FRANK SPRAGUE

Elizabeth Morgan collected this song, published here for the first time, about 1939 from a Colorado farmer somewhere "east of Denver." Mrs. Morgan is the daughter-in-law of the redoubtable Arthur Morgan, former president of Antioch College and an original administrator of the Tennessee Valley Authority.

The room is cold and drear-y, and the fee - ble fire burns low, For "needs" must hoard the pen -nies, the an - gry storm winds blow, A moth - er with her ba - by boy, to soothe his plain -tive cry, pre -

When they shout my ba-by's name and
play the big brass band.

His little face is puny and his
Cheeks are pale and wan,
He's always cold and hungry,
The money is all gone,
His little hands caress her
When his mother starts to cry,
He says, "Let's play at make-believe
And sing our lullaby."

STRANGE FRUIT

By LEWIS ALLEN

A song that electrified everyone who heard it when it was first introduced in the 1930s. Billie Holiday made the greatest recording of it, an interpretation that will probably never be surpassed.

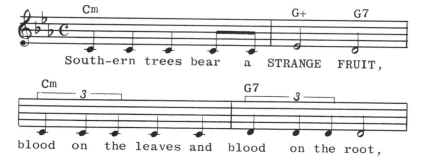

South-ern trees bear a STRANGE FRUIT,
blood on the leaves and blood on the root,

Black bod- y swing-ing in the South-ern breeze,

STRANGE FRUIT hang -ing from the

pop- lar trees. (hum _____)

Pas-tor- al scenes of the gal -lant South, the

bulg - ing eyes and the twist - ed mouth,

Scent of mag-no -lia sweet___ and fresh, and the

sud- den smell of burn-ing flesh!

Here is a fruit for the

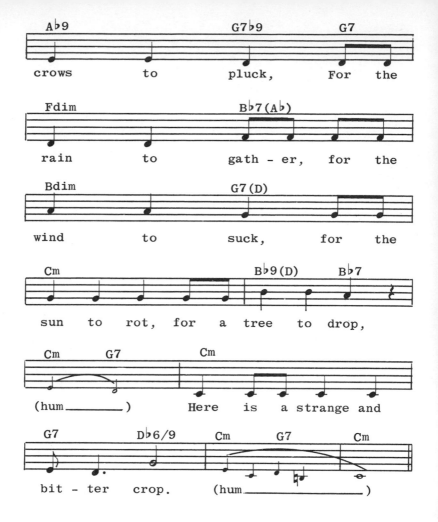

TAKE THIS HAMMER

Words by HUDDIE LEDBETTER

It was unforgettable to see and hear Leadbelly sing this work-song of worksongs, half-dancing to it at the same time, with his powerful body swaying, playing the guitar, and acting out the words.

TAKE THIS HAM - MER

(huh!) car- ry it to the Cap - tain,

(huh!) TAKE THIS HAM - MER

(huh!) car- ry it to the Cap - tain,

(huh!) TAKE THIS HAM - MER

(huh!) car- ry it to the Cap -tain,_____

(huh!) Tell him I'm gone, _____

(huh!) Tell him I'm gone._____ (huh!)

If he ask you (huh!)
"Was I runnin'?"(huh!) (3x)
Tell him I was flyin', (huh!) (2x)

If he ask you (huh!)
"Was I laughin'?"(huh!) (3x)
Tell him I was cryin', (huh!) (2x)

I don't want no (huh!)
Corn bread 'n molasses (huh!) (3x)
Hurts my pride (huh!) (2x)

(repeat first verse)

TALKING ATOM

By VERN PARTLOW

One of the first effective songs after the explosion of the atom bomb.

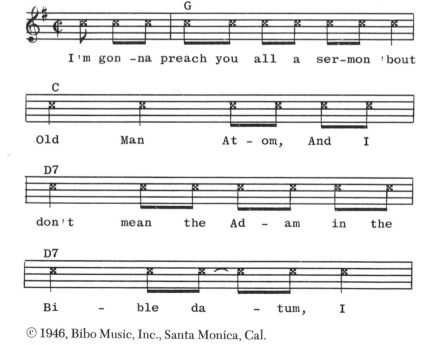

I'm gon -na preach you all a ser-mon 'bout

Old Man At - om, And I

don't mean the Ad - am in the

Bi - ble da - tum, I

don't mean the Ad - am Moth - er
Eve mat - ed, I mean the thing that
sci-ence lib-er- a-ted, You know
Ein-stein said he was scared, and if
he's scared, broth -er,
I'm scared.

Yes, life used to be such a simple
    joy.
The cyclotron was a super toy,
Folks got born, they'd work and
    marry,
And "atom" was a word in the
    dictionary;
And then it happened. . .

These science guys, from every clime
They all pitched in with overtime.
Before you knew it, the job was done;
They'd hitched up the power of the
        doggone sun,
Splitting atoms, right and left,
While the diplomats. . .
Were splitting hairs. . .

Then the cartel crowd, up and put on
        a show,
They're gonna turn back the clock on
        the UNO.
Grab a corner on atoms and mebbe
        extinguish
Every damn atom that can't speak
        English.
Down with foreign born atoms!
America for American atoms!
Step right up, folks, and let's atomize
        world peace. . .

Ah, but the atom's international, in
        spite of hysteria
Flourishes in Utah, also Siberia.
He don't care about politics
Or who got what into whichever fix
All he wants to do. . .
Is sit around. . .
And have his nucleus bombarded by
        neutrons.

Yes, it's up to the people; the atom
        don't care.
You can't fence him in; he's just
        like air.
And whether you're white, black, red,
        or brown,
The question is this, when you boil
        it down:
To be or not to be!
That is the question. . .

And the answer to it all ain't
        military datum,
Like "Who gets there fustest with the
        mostest atoms."
But the people of the world must
        decide their fate.

We got to stick together, or
    disintegrate.
We hold these truths to be self-
    evident:
All men.
Could be cremated equal.

TALKING NEW YORK

By BOB DYLAN

Another early Bob Dylan song, a talking blues, that he used
to sing in Greenwich Village coffee houses.

(Sung or spoken)

Ram - blin' out - a the wild___ west,

leav -in' the towns I love the best,

Thought I'd seen some ups and downs,

till I come in - to New York town.

Peo- ple go - in'

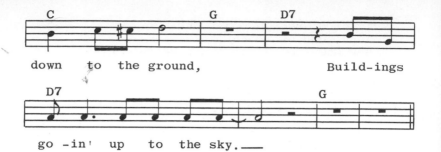

down   to   the   ground,   Build-ings

go -in'   up   to   the   sky.___

Winter time in New York town,
The wind blowin' snow around,
Walk around with nowhere to go,
Somebody could freeze right to the bone,
I froze right to the bone.
"New York Times" said it was the
Coldest winter in seventeen years,
I didn't feel so cold then.

I swung on to my old guitar,
Grabbed hold of a subway car,
And after a rocking, reeling, rolling ride,
I landed up on the downtown side;
Greenwich Village.

I walked down there and ended up
In one of them coffee houses on the block.
Got on the stage to sing and play,
Man there said, "Come back some other day,
You sound like a hill-billy;
We want folk singers here."

Well, I got a harmonica job, begun to play,
Blowin' my lungs out for a dollar a day.
I blowed inside out and upside down;
The man there said he loved m' sound.
Dollar a day's worth.

And after weeks and weeks of hangin' around,
I finally got a job in New York town,
In a bigger place, bigger money too,
Even joined the Union and paid m' dues.

Now, a very great man once said
That some people rob you with a fountain pen.
It didn't take too long to find out
Just what he was talkin' about.

A lot of people don't have
Much food on their table,
But they got a lot of forks 'n' knives,
And they gotta cut somethin'.

So one mornin' when the sun was warm,
I rambled out of New York town,
Pulled my cap down over my eyes
And headed out for the western skies.
So long, New York.
Howdy, East Orange.

TALKING UNION

By LEE HAYS, MILLARD LAMPELL, and PETE SEEGER

The famous talking blues by the Almanac Singers.

Talking Blues, steady beat

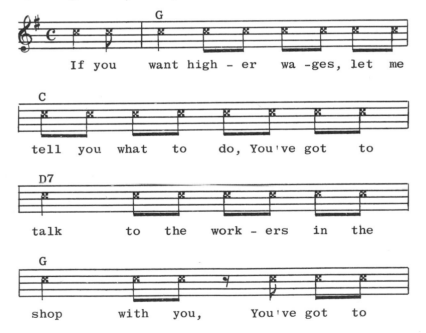

build   you   a   un - ion,   got   to

make   it   strong,   But   if   you

all   stick   to - geth - er,   boys,

'twon't   be   long,   You'll get

short -er   ho -urs,   bet -ter

work- ing   con- di - tions,   va   -

ca - tions with   pay, ____

Take your kids to the

sea - shore.

It ain't quite this simple, so I'd better explain
Just why you've got to ride on the union train,
'Cause if you wait for the boss to raise your pay
We'll all be a-waiting till the judgment day --
We'll all be buried. . . gone to heaven. . .
St. Peter'll be the foreman then.

Now you know you're underpaid but the boss says
    you ain't,
He speeds up the work till you're about to faint.
You may be down and out but you ain't beaten...
You can pass out a leaflet and call a meetin'..
Talk it over...speak your mind...
Decide to do something about it.

Suppose they're working you
So hard it's just outrageous,
And they're paying you all starvation wages,
You go to the boss, and the boss will yell,
"Before I raise your pay
I'll see you all in Hell."

'Course, the boss may persuade
Some poor damn fool
To go to your meeting and act like a stool,
But you can always tell a stool, boys,
And that's a fact,
He's got a yellow streak a-running down his back.
He doesn't have to stool,
He'll always get along,
On what he steals out of blind men's cups.

He's puffing a big seegar, feeling might slick,
'Cause he thinks he's got your union licked,
Well, he looks out the window
And what does he see,
But a thousand pickets and they all agree,
He's a bastard, unfair, slave-driver,
Bet he beats his wife.

305

Now, boys, you've come to the hardest time,
The boss will try to pust your picket line,
He'll call out the po-lice
And the National Guard,
They'll raid your meetings,
They'll hit you on the head,
They'll call every one of you a Goddamn Red,
Unpatriotic, agitators,
Send 'em back where they come from.

But out in De-troit, here's what they found,
And out in Pittsburgh, here's what they found,
And out in Akron, here's what they found,
And up in Toronto, here's what they found:
That if you don't let Red-baiting break you up,
And if you don't let vigilantes break you up,
And if you don't let race hatred break you up,
And if you don't let stool-pigeons break you up,
You'll win. . . what I mean. . .
Take it easy. . . but take it!

THIS LITTLE LIGHT OF MINE

Modern words of love and peace were tacked onto an older spiritual, often sung by the members of the Student Peace Union of the 1960s.

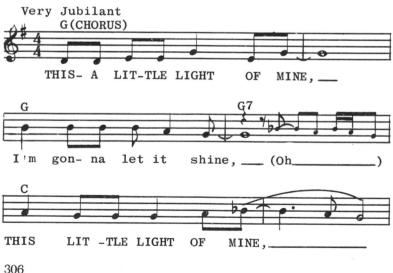

Very Jubilant

G (CHORUS)

THIS- A LIT-TLE LIGHT OF MINE, ___

G   G7

I'm gon- na let it shine, ___ (Oh_____)

C

THIS LIT -TLE LIGHT OF MINE,_____

I'm gon-na let it shine, ____ (Oh ____)

THIS LIT - TLE LIGHT OF MINE, ____

I'm gon - na let it shine, __ let it shine, __

____ let it shine, ____ let it shine, __

The light that shines is the

light of love, __ Lights the dark - ness

from a -bove, ____ It shines on me and it

shines on you, __ Shows what the pow'r of love can __ do, I'm gon - na shine my light __ both far and near, __ I'm gon - na shine my light both bright and clear, __ Where there's a dark cor - ner in this land, __ I'm gon - na let my lit - tle light shine.

We've got the light of freedom,
We're gonna let it shine, etc...

Deep down in the South,
We're gonna let it shine, etc...

Down in Birmingham (Mississippi, Alabama,etc...)
We're gonna let it shine, etc...

Everywhere I go,
I'm gonna let it shine, etc...

All in the jail house, etc...

TIMES GETTIN' HARD

One of the most poignant tunes from our rich lode of folk melodies. A Depression song, stark and beautiful and sad as the sharecroppers' faces, white and black, photographed by Walker Evans and others in the 1930s.

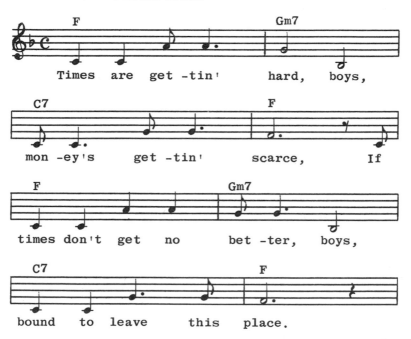

F   Gm7
Times are get -tin'   hard,   boys,

C7   F
mon -ey's   get -tin'   scarce,   If

F   Gm7
times don't get   no   bet -ter,   boys,

C7   F
bound   to leave   this   place.

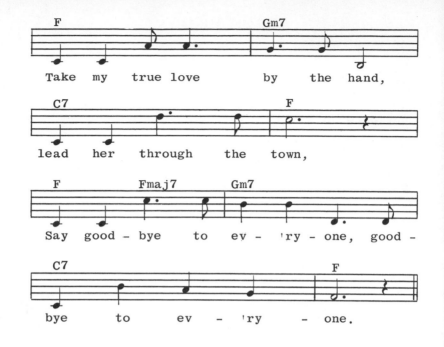

Take my true love by the hand,
lead her through the town,
Say good – bye to ev – 'ry – one, good –
bye to ev – 'ry – one.

Take my Bible from the bed,
Shotgun from the wall,
Take old Sal and hitch her up,
The wagon for to haul.
Pile the chairs and beds up high,
Let nothing drag the ground,
Sal can pull and we can push,
We're bound to leave this town.

Made a crop a year ago,
It withered to the ground,
Tried to get some credit,
But the banker turned me down,
Goin' to Califor-ni-ay,
Where everything is green,
Goin' to have the best old farm
That you have ever seen.

TOM JOAD

Woody Guthrie took the folk melody "John Hardy" after seeing the great film *The Grapes of Wrath* and wrote this ballad based on the picture. Woody, of course, came from the same background as the migrants in John Steinbeck's novel.

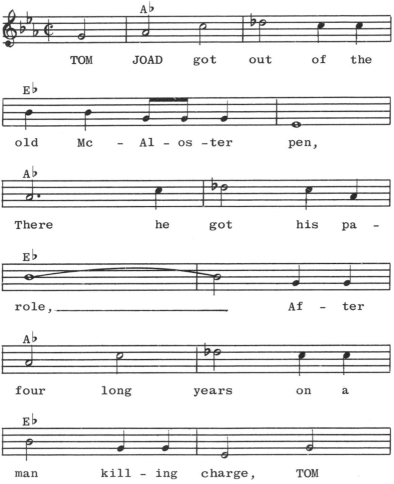

TOM JOAD got out of the old Mc - Al - os -ter pen, There he got his pa - role,_____ Af - ter four long years on a man kill - ing charge, TOM

TRO-© Copyright 1960 and 1963, Ludlow Music, Inc., New York, N.Y. Used by permission.

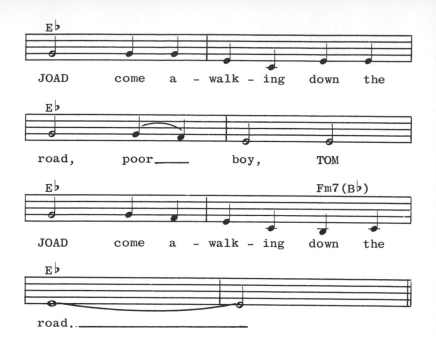

JOAD come a - walk - ing down the road, poor____ boy, TOM JOAD come a - walk - ing down the road..____

TOM JOAD he met a truck driving man,
There he caught him a ride,
He said: "I just got loose from McAlester's pen
On a charge called homicide.
A charge called homicide."

That truck rolled away in a cloud of dust,
Tommy turned his face toward home,
He met Preacher Casey and they had a little drink,
But they found that his family they was gone,
He found that his family they was gone.

He found his mother's old fashioned shoe,
Found his daddy's hat,
And he found little Muley and Muley said:
"They've been tractored out by the cats.
They've been tractored out by the cats."

TOM JOAD walked down to the neighbor's farm,
Found his family.
They took Preacher Casey and loaded in a car
And his mother said: "We got to git away."
His mother said: "We got to git away."

Now the twelve of the Joads
Made a might heavy load,
But Grandpa Joad did cry,
He picked up a handful of land in his hand,
Said: "I'm stayin' with the farm till I die.
Yes, I'm stayin' with my farm till I die."

They fed him short ribs and
Coffee and soothing syrup,
And Grandpa Joad did die,
They buried Grandpa Joad by the side of the road,
Buried Grandma on the California side,
They buried Grandma on the California side.

They stood on a mountain
And they looked to the West,
And it looked like the Promised Land,
That bright green valley
With a river running through,
There was work for every single hand,
They thought,
There was work for every single hand.

The Joads rolled away to Jungle Camp,
There they cooked a stew.
And the hungry little kids of Jungle Camp
Said: "We'd like to have some too."
Said: "We'd like to have some too."

Now a deputy Sheriff fired loose at a man,
Shot a woman in the back.
Before he could take his aim again
Preacher Casey dropped him in his track.
Preacher Casey dropped him in his track.

They handcuffed Casey and they took him to jail,
And then he got away.
And he met TOM JOAD on the old river bridge,
And these few words he did say, poor boy.
These few words he did say.

"I preached for the Lord a mighty long time.
Preached about the rich and the poor.
Us workin' folks is all get together
'Cause we ain't got a chance anymore.
We ain't got a chance anymore."

The deputies come and Tom and Casey run
To the bridge where the water run down.
But the vigilantes they hit Casey with a club,
They laid Preacher Casey on the ground.
They laid Preacher Casey on the ground.

TOM JOAD he grabbed that deputy's club,
Hit him over the head.
TOM JOAD took flight in the dark rainy night,
A deputy and a preacher lying dead.   Two men.
A deputy and a preacher lying dead.

Tom run back where his mother was asleep,
He woke her up out of bed,
Then he kissed goodbye
To the mother that he loved,
Said what Preacher Casey said, TOM JOAD,
He said what Preacher Casey said.

"Ev'rybody might be just one big soul
Well it looks that-a-way to me.
Everywhere that you look in the day or night
That's where I'm gonna be, Ma,
That's where I'm gonna be.

Wherever little children are hungry and cry;
Wherever people ain't free,
Wherever men are fightin' for their rights,
That's where I'm gonna be, Ma,
That's where I'm gonna be.

TOO OLD TO WORK

By JOE GLAZER

Inspired by the industrial unions' push in 1949-1950 for workers
pensions, their slogan being, "Too Old to Work, Too Young to
Die."

With steady rhythm

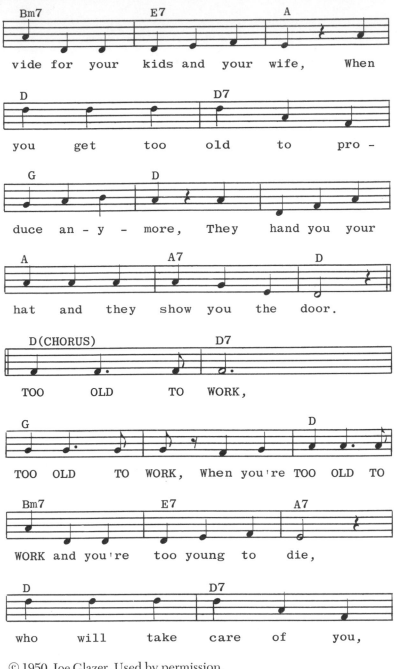

315

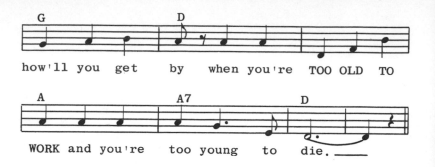

how'll you get by when you're TOO OLD TO

WORK and you're too young to die. ____

You don't ask for favors
When your life is through,
You've got a right
To what's coming to you,
Your boss get a pension
When he is too old,
You help him retire,
You're out in the cold.

They even put horses to pasture,
They feed them on hay,
Even machines get retired some day,
The bosses get pensions
When their days are through,
Fat pensions for them, brother,
Nothing for you.

There's no easy answer,
There's no easy cure,
Dreaming won't change it,
That's one thing for sure,
But fighting together
We'll get there some day,
And when we have won,
We will no longer say:

THE UAW-CIO

By BALDWIN HAWES

One of the most inspired and original of all labor songs, this was written mostly by Baldwin Hawes, during the early days of our entry into World War II.

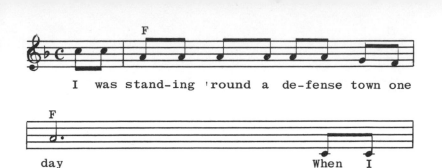
I was stand-ing 'round a de-fense town one

day   When   I

thought I   o - ver - heard   a   sol - dier

say: "Ev - 'ry

tank   in   our   camp   has   that

U.   A.   DOU -BLE - U. stamp,   And   I'm

U.   A.   DOU- BLE - U. too I'm proud to   say."

CHORUS

It's the   U.   A.   DOU- BLE- U. C. I.   O.

makes the ar - my roll and go,

Turn -ing out the jeeps and tanks and

air -planes ev - 'ry day, It's the

U. A. DOU -BLE - U. C. I. O.

makes the ar - my roll and go, puts

wheels _____ on the U. S. A.

I was there when the union came to town,
I was there when old Henry Ford went down,
I was standing by Gate Four
When I heard the people roar:
"They ain't gonna kick the autoworkers around."

I was there on that cold December day,
When we heard about Pearl Harbor far away,
I was down in Cadillac Square
When the union rallied there,
To put those plans for pleasure cars away.

There'll be a union label in Berlin
When those union boys in uniform march in;
And rolling in the ranks there'll be UAW tanks:
Roll Hitler out and roll the union in.

UHURU

The title is a common greeting in West Africa, and means "freedom," as indeed do all the words in this chant.

U - hu U - HU - RU Ai -

ye Free - dom!

U - hu U - HU - RU Ai -

ye Free - dom!

U - hu U - HU - RU Ai -

ye Free - dom!

U - HU - RU! U -

HU - RU O Sa - wa - ba!

U - HU - RU! Ai - ye! Ai -

ye! Ai - ye! Free - dom!

UNION MAID

By WOODY GUTHRIE

"Redwing" is one of the most parodied songs in American folk-lore. Woody Guthrie used the old tune to fashion his famous song during the great wave of union organizing in the 1930s.

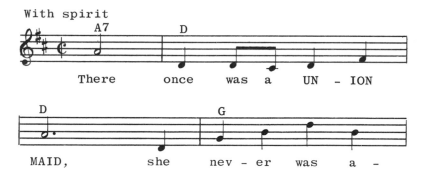

With spirit

There once was a UN - ION

MAID, she nev - er was a -

fraid   of   goons   and   ginks   and

com - pa - ny   finks   and   the

de - pu - ty   sher - iffs that

made   the raid. She   went   to   the Un - ion

Hall   when   a   meet-ing   it   was called,   And

when   the   com -p'ny   boys   came 'round she

al - ways   stood   her   ground.

CHORUS

Oh,   you can't scare   me, I'm stick-ing to   the

Un - ion, I'm stick-ing to the
Un - ion, I'm stick -ing to the
Un - ion,_____ Oh, you can't scare
me, I'm stick-ing to the Un - ion,
I'm stick-ing to the Un - ion_____
_____. till the day I die._____

This Union Maid was wise
To the tricks of company spies
She couldn't be fooled by company stools;
She'd always organize the guys.
She'd always get her way
When she struck for higher pay:
She'd show her card to the National Guard
And this is what she'd say: (Cho.)

You girls who want to be free
Just take a tip from me!
Get you a man who's a Union man
And join the Ladies Auxiliary.
Married life ain't hard
When you've got a Union card.
A Union man has a happy life
When he's got a Union wife. (Cho.)

UNITED NATIONS MAKE A CHAIN (HOLD ON)

By TOM GLAZER

I wrote these words to the spiritual, "Mary Had a Golden Chain" in Washington, D.C., in the early 1940s.

U -NIT - ED   NA - TIONS make   a
chain,   Ev - 'ry   link   is   free -dom's
name,   Keep   your   hand   on____   that
peace,   hold   on._____
CHORUS
Hold   on, _____   hold

on, _____ keep your hand on___ that

peace, hold on. _____

Freedom's name is mighty sweet,
All free men have got to meet. . .

If somebody ever throws that bomb,
You can't go runnin' home to Mom. . .

One thing's gettin' mighty clear,
There ain't no hiding place down here. . .

United Nations make a chain,
Every link is freedom's name. . .

THE UNIVERSAL SOLDIER

By BUFFY SAINTE-MARIE

Probably Buffy Sainte-Marie's most popular composition.

He's five foot two and he's

six feet ___ four, He

fights with mis -siles and with

spears,_____ He's

all of thir - ty one and he's

on - ly sev - en - teen, He's been a

sol - dier for a thou - sand

years._____

He's a Catholic, a Hindu,
An atheist, a Jain,
A Buddhist and a Baptist
And a Jew,
And he knows he shouldn't kill
And he knows he always will,
Kill you for me, my friend,
And me for you.

And he's fighting for Canada,
He's fighting for France,
He's fighting for the U.S.A.,
And he's fighting for the Russians,
And he's fighting for Japan,
And he thinks we'll put an end to war that way.

And he's fighting for democracy,
He's fighting for the Reds,
He says it's for the peace of all,
He's the one who must decide
Who's to live and who's to die,
And he never sees the writing on the wall.

But without him how could Hitler
Have condemned him at Dachau,
Without him Caesar would have stood alone,
He's the one who gives his body
As a weapon of the war,
And without him all this killing can't go on.

He's the UNIVERSAL SOLDIER
And he really is to blame,
His orders come from far away no more,
They come from him and you and me,
And brothers, can't you see
This is not the way we put an end to war.

WALK IN PEACE

By SIR LANCELOT

There was a great wave of popularity of Calypso songs in the early and middle 1940s, and several singers with very fancy names were heard in nightclubs. One of them was Sir Lancelot, who wrote this beautiful peace song.

Ev-'ry-one who's been to school___

heard a-bout the Gold-en Rule,___

It's a sto-ry old but true,___ Do un-to

oth- ers as you'd have them do un - to you, ___

Now the way it looks to me ___

it's a case of re - ci -

proc - i - ty, ___ We must ob -

serve it im - plic - it - ly, ___

___ if we hope to save the

world from ca - lam - i - ty. ___

CHORUS

For it's as sim - ple as one and

one   makes two, ___ Do un - to

oth - ers as you'd have them   do

un - to   you, ___   It's   the

on - ly way that wars will cease, ___ and

men of good will shall WALK IN   PEACE. ___

We must learn to give and take,
If a better world we hope to make.
How can you teach Hungarians democracy,
While at home you practise racial bigotry?
We must get the other fellow's point of view;
He has a right to his opinions, too.
You know, the "know-how" of being free
Is not a Yankee monopoly.

We condemn Russians for tyranny,
And denial to the press of liberty.
But tell me this one thing, candidly:
Is Greece, or Spain, or even China, free?
And black men in this great democracy,
Do they walk with noble dignity?
Or do they hang their heads in shame,
And torture their souls in a Jim Crow train?

328

What a pity it is to see
Churches in our beloved country
Denying the brotherhood of man
By bowing to the doctrine of segregation.
We must practice what we preach,
If we would Poles and Balkans teach,
That in our great land the world might see
A shining example of democracy.

WANDERIN'

If I remember correctly, a singer named Michael Loring introduced this lovely folksong to New York and the rest of the country in the late 1930s or early 1940s. Others have added their own verses.

My dad - dy is an en - gi -neer, my
broth - er drives a hack, my
sis - ter takes in wash - ing and the
ba - by balls the jack, And it
looks like I'm nev -er gon- na cease my
WAN - DER - IN'.

I've been a-wanderin', early and late,
New York City to the Golden Gate,
An' it looks like I'm
Never gonna cease my WANDERIN'.

Been a-workin' in the army, workin' on a farm,
All I got to show for it is the muscle in my arm,
An' it looks like I'm
Never gonna cease my WANDERIN'.

Snakes in the ocean, eels in the sea,
Red headed woman made a fool out of me,
An' it looks like I'm
Never gonna cease my WANDERIN'.

A WELL-RESPECTED MAN

By RAY DAVIES

A rock and roll hit song with not so faint overtones of anti-organization satire. Recorded by a British group called the Kinks in 1967-1968.

'Cause he gets up in the morn - ing, And he goes to work at nine,___ ___ And he comes back home at five thir - ty,___ Gets the

same train ev - 'ry time, _____ 'Cause his

world is built on punc- tu - al - i - ty,_

_ it nev -er fails._

And he's oh, so good, and he's

oh, so fine, and he's

oh, so health - y in his

bod - y and his mind, He's A

WELL RE - SPECT - ED MAN a - bout_ town,

do - ing the best____ things

so con -ser - va-tive- ly. _____

And his mother goes to meetings,
While his father paws the maid,
And she stirs the tea with counsellors
While discussing Foreign Trade,
And she passes looks as well as Bills
At every suave young man. (Chorus)

And he likes his own back-yard,
And he likes his fags the best,
And he's better than the rest,
And his own sweat smells the best,
And he hopes to grab his Father's loot
When his Pater passes on. (Chorus)

And he plays the stocks and shares,
And he goes to the regatta;
He adores the girl next door,
'Cause he's trying to get'at her,
But his Mother knows the best about
The matrimonial stakes. (Chorus)

WE SHALL NOT BE MOVED

One of the most popular of all union songs, next to "Solidarity
Forever." It is based on an old hymn, "I Shall Not Be Moved,"
itself based on a line from Jeremiah in the Bible: "Blessed is
the man who trusteth in the Lord, for he shall be as a tree
planted by the waters." First sung in 1931 by miners. Newer
verses keep being added and sung.

We are fighting for our freedom,
WE SHALL NOT BE MOVED...

We are black and white together,
WE SHALL NOT BE MOVED...

We will stand and fight together,
WE SHALL NOT BE MOVED...

The Government is behind us,
WE SHALL NOT BE MOVED...

Our parks are intergrating,
WE SHALL NOT BE MOVED...

We're sunning on the beaches,
WE SHALL NOT BE MOVED...

WE SHALL OVERCOME

New words and arrangement by ZILPHIA HORTON,
FRANK HAMILTON, GUY CARAWAN, and
PETE SEEGER

The unofficial anthem of the Freedom Movement of the 1960s. It is a sight to see, on television, black activists and white politicians, arms linked, swaying to and fro, singing this song together as I mentioned in the Introduction. Royalties derived from this composition are being contributed to The Freedom Movement under the trusteeship of the writers.

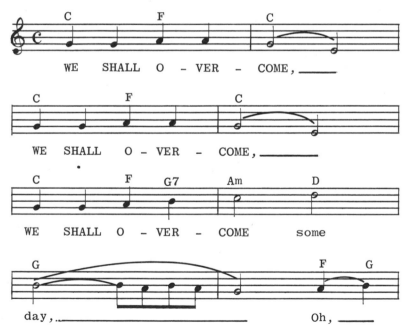

WE SHALL O - VER - COME, ____

WE SHALL O - VER - COME, ____

WE SHALL O - VER - COME some

day, ____ Oh, ____

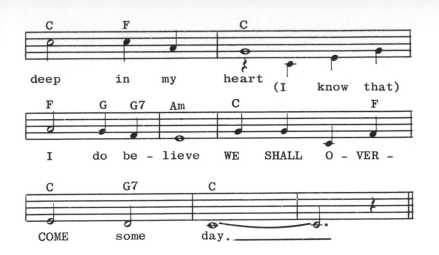

deep in my heart (I know that) I do believe WE SHALL O - VER - COME some day.

We'll walk hand in hand,
We'll walk hand in hand,
We'll walk hand in hand someday,
Oh, deep in my heart
I do believe
WE SHALL OVERCOME someday.

We shall live in peace, etc.

We shall all be free, etc.

We shall end Jim Crow, etc.

We are not afraid, etc.

The Lord will see us through, etc.

We are not alone, etc.

The whole wide world around, etc.

The truth will make us free, etc.

We shall ban the bomb, etc.

Black and white together, etc.

WE SHALL OVERCOME, etc.

WHAT HAVE THEY DONE TO THE RAIN

By MALVINA REYNOLDS

This song, along with Bob Dylan's "A Hard Rain's Goin' to Fall," are two powerful comments on rain polluted by atomic bomb explosions.

WHAT HAVE THEY DONE TO THE RAIN?
WHAT HAVE THEY DONE TO THE RAIN?

Just a lit - tle boy,

stand - ing in the rain, The

gen - tle rain that

falls for years, And the

grass is gone, the boy dis-ap-pears And

rain keeps fall-ing like help-less tears, and

WHAT HAVE THEY DONE TO THE RAIN?

WHERE HAVE ALL THE FLOWERS GONE

By PETE SEEGER

Pete Seeger's biggest hit song so far. There was even a hit record in German.

338

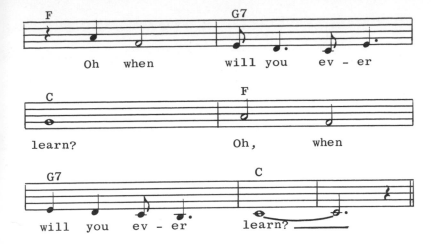

Where have all the young girls gone?
Long time passing.
Where have all the young girls gone?
Long time ago.
Where have all the young girls gone?
They've taken husbands everyone.
Oh, when will you ever learn?
Oh, when will you ever learn?

Where have all the young men gone?
Long time passing.
Where have all the young men gone?
Long time ago.
Where have all the young men gone?
They're all in uniform.
Oh, when will you ever learn?
Oh, when will you ever learn?

Where have all the soldiers gone?
Long time passing.
Where have all the soldiers gone?
Long time ago.
Where have all the soldiers gone?
They've gone to graveyards, every one.
Oh, when will they ever learn?
Oh, when will they ever learn?

Where have all the graveyards gone?
Long time passing.
Where have all the graveyards gone?
Long time ago.
Where have all the graveyards gone?
They're covered with flowers, every one.
Oh, when will they ever learn?
Oh, when will they ever learn?

WHERE HAVE ALL THE FLOWERS GONE?
Long time passing.
WHERE HAVE ALL THE FLOWERS GONE?
Long time ago.
WHERE HAVE ALL THE FLOWERS GONE?
Young girls picked them, every one,
Oh, when will they ever learn?
Oh, when will they ever learn?

WHICH SIDE ARE YOU ON

Words by FLORENCE REESE

The famous challenge of the 1930s, with words by Florence Reese, and with many new verses that keep cropping up here and there as written for various occasions, including some below by James Farmer.

Come all of you good work - ers, good news to you I'll tell, Of how the good old un - ion has

come in here to dwell.

Bm (CHORUS)　　A　　Bm

WHICH　SIDE　ARE　YOU　ON?

Bm　　F#7　　Bm

WHICH SIDE　ARE　YOU　ON?

Bm　　A　　Bm

WHICH SIDE　ARE　YOU　ON?

Bm　　F#7　　Bm

WHICH　SIDE　ARE　YOU　ON?

Don't scab for the bosses,
Don't listen to their lies,
Us poor folks haven't got a chance
Unless we organize.

They say in Harlan County,
There are no neutrals there,
You'll either be a union man,
Or a thug for J.H.Blair.

Oh, workers, can you stand it?
Oh, tell me how you can,
Will you be a lousy scab,
Or will you be a man?

My daddy was a miner,
And I'm a miner's son,
And I'll stick with the union
Till every battle's won.

WHO'S NEXT

Another deft bit of social satire by Tom Lehrer.

First we got the bomb and that was good, 'cause we love peace and moth -er- hood,__ Then Rus-sia got the bomb, but that's o - kay,___ 'cause the bal - ance of pow - er's main - tained that way. WHO'S NEXT? Then

France got the bomb, but don't you grieve 'cause

they're on our side (I be-lieve —)

Chi - na got the bomb but

have no fears, — 'Cause they

can't wipe us out for at

least five years. WHO'S NEXT?

Then In - do -ne -sia claimed that they were

gon - na get one an - y day, — South

Af - ri - ca — wants two, that's right,

one   for   the   black   and   one —

— for   the white. WHO'S   NEXT?

E - gypt's   gon - na

get — one   too, ———   Just   to

use   on   you ——   know   who, ———   So

Is - ra - el's get   - ting tense,

wants   one   in   self———   de-fense,   "The

Lord's our shep-herd," says the psalm, but just in case we bet-ter get a bomb. WHO'S NEXT?

Lux - em -bourg is next to go, And (who knows?) may - be Mon -a - co.__ We'll try to stay__ se - rene and calm __ when Al- a - ba - ma gets the bomb.__ WHO'S NEXT? WHO'S NEXT? WHO'S NEXT?__ WHO'S NEXT?

WINNSBORO COTTON MILL BLUES

A great song, collected at the Southern School for Workers in North Carolina in 1939. To "doff" is to remove filled bobbins from spinning frames in the mill.

Old man Sar - gent,
sit - ting at the desk, The
damn' old fool won't give us a rest, ___
He'd take the nick - els off a
dead man's eyes to buy Co- ca Co -la and
Es - ki - mo pies. ___

CHORUS
I got the blues, I got the blues, I got THE

When I die, don't bury me at all,
Just hang me up on the spool-room wall;
Place a knotter in my hand,
So I can spool in the Promised Land.

When I die, don't bury me deep,
Bury me down on Six Hundred Street;
Place a bobbin in each hand
So I can doff in the Promised Land.

WOKE UP THIS MORNING
(WITH MY MIND SET ON FREEDOM)

Additional lyrics and music arranged
by ROBERT ZELLNER

A traditional tune with words by SNCC members and others.

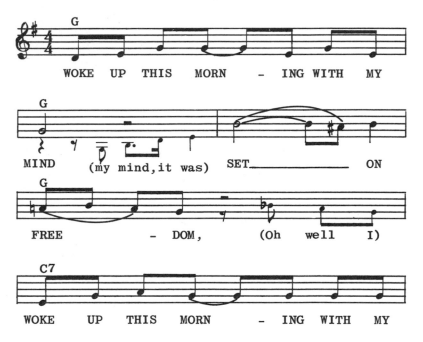

MIND_____ SET_____ ON FREE — DOM, (Oh well I) WOKE UP THIS MORN — ING WITH MY MIND (My mind, it was) SET_____ ON FREE — DOM, Hal - le - lu, Hal- le-lu, Hal-le- lu, Hal- le-lu, Hal- le- lu — jah!

Ain't no harm to keep your mind stayed on freedom,
Ain't no harm to keep your mind stayed on freedom,
Ain't no harm to keep your mind stayed on freedom,
Hallelu, hallelu, hallelu, hallelu, hallelujah!

Walkin' and talkin'
With my mind stayed on freedom, etc...

Singin' and prayin'
With my mind stayed on freedom, etc...

Doin' the twist
With my mind stayed on freedom, etc...

ZUM GALI GALI

An infectious worksong converted into a song of peace. In
English the words say, more or less: The pioneer is for his
work; work is for the pioneer. The pioneer is for his sweetheart;
his sweetheart is for the pioneer. Peace is for all people; all
people are for peace.

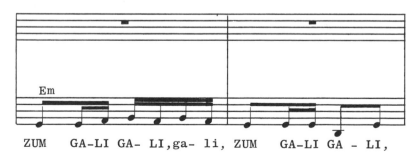

He-cha-lutz le - man a- vo-dah,

ZUM GA-LI GA-LI,ga- li, ZUM GA-LI GA - LI,

a- vo- dah le - man he-cha-lutz.

ZUM GA-LI GA-LI, ga-li, ZUM GA-LI GA - LI.

A-vo-dah le'man he-cha-lutz
He-cha-lutz le'man a-vo-dah.

He-cha-lutz le'man ha-b'tulah;
Ha-b'tulah le'man he-cha-lutz.

Ha-shalom le'man ha'amin
Ha'amin le'man ha-shalom.

351